D1315435

DEDICATION

This book is dedicated to the Norwegian American Hospital Foundation for its humanitarian work in meeting the needs of the sick and medically underserved in this community and in various countries throughout the world. Through the auspices of the Foundation, medical missions in support of the sick and infirm have been sent to Bolivia, Colombia, the Dominican Republic, Ecuador, Mexico, Peru, and the Philippines. And it is only through the generous support and vision of the Foundation, that we are able to publish this book.

Contents

ACKNOWLEDGMENTS

A book of this magnitude and scope could not possibly be completed without the assistance and input of many people. I am indebted to all for their help and good wishes.

Primarily, I wish to acknowledge the invaluable assistance of Marge Del Rosso, longtime secretary to the Director of the Nursing School and currently archivist at Norwegian American Hospital without whose help this book could never have been written. Not only did Ms. Del Rosso give me free reign over her priceless copies of the longtime hospital publication, the *Lamp*, dating back to the 1940s, and other hospital literature, but she spent hours literally combing through her records for names, phone numbers and other material on various nursing school alumnae, doctors, present and past. In addition, she was one of several kind enough to read the manuscript and to offer many excellent suggestions on dates and factual material.

I am further indebted to all the others who took the time to read the manuscript, including Clarence Nagelvoort, Immediate Past President of Norwegian American Hospital, Mary Toma, Executive Vice President, Per Ohrstrom, Norwegian Consul General in Chicago, Dr. Pedro Lopez, former medical director and chief of staff, and especially Edith DeYoung, former administrative assistant to several hospital executives, whose comments were especially keen and insightful.

Also of great help were former board members William Korsvik and Art Bagge. Mr. Korsvik offered numerous suggestions for sources of material and offered several books for my use which proved especially helpful, including Birger Osland's autobiography, *A Long Way from Stavanger*, and Professor Odd Lovoll's book on Norwegian settlers in America, *A Portrait of Norwegian Americans Today*. This book proved a treasure trove of material on the early Norwegian settlers in Chicago and the founding of the hospital in 1893.

I also would like to thank the many men and women, previously or currently connected with the hospital, who were kind enough to share their memories of the hospital, in compiling Exhibit 1 – The Interview Section.

Of great assistance was the staff of the Norwegian American Historical Association, in Northfield, Minnesota, who supplied priceless photos dating back to the hospital's founding, as well as back issues of *Skandinaven*, the primary Norwegian publication in Chicago in the '50s and later. They include Ruth Hanold Crane, Assistant Secretary, Mr. Forrest Brown, Archivist, and Lloyd Hustvedt, Secretary.

Ms. Torun Soknes, a Norwegian graduate student working on her master's thesis, was kind enough to share her research on several women physicians who were among the early members of the hospital medical staff around the turn of the century.

Also very helpful was Ms. Ellen Engseth, Director of the Swedish American Historical Society, in Chicago, who was kind enough to supply biographical material on several pioneer physicians at Norwegian American Hospital, or the Norwegian Lutheran Tabitha Hospital, as it was known in those days.

Much of the material in Exhibit 2 – Great Men and Women of Norwegian American Hospital – appeared originally in the hospital publication, the *Lamp*, which was published between 1940 into the '90s.

Another who was very helpful was Mr. William Lichtenstein, who supplied much of the material on his father, Dr. Emanuel Lichtenstein, for many years one of the outstanding surgeons at Norwegian American, who died in 1970.

Ms. Carmen Vazquez, of the hospital's Community Relations Department, was of great assistance in tracking down many of the photos appearing in this book.

And I cannot overlook the numerous services supplied by the staff of former hospital Board Chairman Norman R. Dahl in expediting the work on the manuscript. They are Maritza Vargas, and former staff members: Marie Granados, and Lynn Pilolla.

Finally, I must acknowledge the tremendous contribution of the author, Mr. Norman R. Dahl, the former hospital Chairman of the Board, who was the instigator of this book and who guided its progress every step of the way from concept through manuscript, and into production and distribution.

To all of these individuals, and to many I may inadvertently have overlooked, my deepest thanks for your encouragement and active support.

Terry Sacks, Editor

Welcome to *Heal the Sick:*
The Story of Norwegian American Hospital

T his book is the result of many months of effort and planning. It details the history of the hospital, from its origin, through the years of building and expansion in the '20s, followed by the Depression years, the war years, the days of rebuilding and expansion of the '50s and '60s, through current times, and ends with our hopes for the future. Throughout this history, the players may have changed: the Norwegians who founded the hospital are long gone and the hospital now serves a largely Latino population from which it derives most of its patients and support. But the goals remain the same: to provide the best in health care and service to the community that technology and our resources can offer.

My connections to Norwegian American Hospital go back many years. As a lad in elementary school, from about 1937, I would participate in the big May 17 parade in Humboldt Park celebrating Norwegian independence. It was an exciting and eagerly awaited event for the thousands who participated and the onlookers, many of them residents of this very Humboldt Park Community.

Following the parade, we would often remain in the park where we would participate in a ball game, go boating in the beautiful lagoon or just stroll around that wonderful park. It was during the '40s that I first got to know Norwegian American Hospital since some of my boyhood chums had family members who were employed there. And many of my neighborhood friends would visit there because we knew several of the young persons in training there.

Who could have seen at the time how this hospital would grow to become a magnificent two building complex, covering nearly two square blocks with a beautiful campus and plenty of adjacent parking leading directly to the park, just west of the hospital.

Not that the hospital has not had its share of crises – the Depression for one. The hospital had just completed a vast building program of the '20s and was heavily in debt. Times were tough for all of us and for Norwegian American too. Dozens of hospitals, the nation over, were closing and for a while it looked as though Norwegian might be forced to close too.

Fortunately, we had two very capable leaders who were able to pull us through those dark days – Olaus Krabol, the hospital's president through the '20s and early '30s, and Birger Osland, who followed and controlled the reins in the mid-'30s through the early '40s. Through scrimping, scraping and cutting every ounce of fat out of the budget, we were able to come through, the stronger and better for the experience.

It was but one of several crises the hospital has faced head on in its 105-year history, starting with the split in leadership, almost at the outset of the hospital, to the dark days of the Depression and the strike of 1972, which for several weeks threatened to close the hospital down. This was followed by the sharp slump in admissions and revenue of the late '70s and the early '80s, stemming largely from new procedures instituted by Medicaid in the reimbursement of hospitals. It is all detailed in the pages of this book.

Accompanying the external changes in the hospital's appearance and a constant shuffling and reshuffling of new and expanding departments for space, were many changes in technology. For example, when I was a lad, cataract surgery was a much dreaded procedure entailing a hospital stay of two weeks, and the use of sandbags placed strategically between the pillows to prevent the patient from moving around. Today this same procedure, including the implant of lenses, can be done in a matter of hours and the patient is discharged the same day.

The hospital was changing ethnically as well. Even when I was a boy – in the mid '30s – the composition of the medical staff had changed from one almost solely Norwegian and Scandinavian – to one which had many Jewish, Polish, and Italian physicians on staff. Many of these were brilliant men and women who would have been a credit to any hospital.

By the late '60s and early '70s, as documented in these pages, the ethnic makeup of the community had again changed gradually to one comprised largely of residents of Latino background.

And the Norwegian pioneer physicians, staff members and trustees, who guided this hospital for much of its lifespan, are long gone except for a few members of the Board of Trustees.

But the Norwegian flag continues to fly at both main entrances to the hospital and the hospital name continues to be Norwegian American. Why? Because it was these Norwegian pioneers, who through their vision, hard work and sweat, and perseverance, in good times and bad, enabled this hospital to continue to serve the Humboldt Park and greater Northwestside communities. They provided the structure and the foundation upon which this hospital has been built and continues to grow so magnificently.

It is quite possible that since Norwegian American Hospital and Lutheran Deaconess, the forerunner of the present Lutheran General Hospital, shared at one time many of the same doctors and the same common ancestor, the Norwegian Lutheran Tabitha Society, we could have mended our fences and joined Lutheran Deaconess in their decision to leave the city for greener pastures, so to speak. But that would have meant abandoning our Humboldt Park and Northwestside patients. Who would have picked up the slack and provided the health care that was so desperately needed in the area?

The point is that though the racial and ethnic makeup of the community has changed and continues to change, Norwegian American Hospital has never wavered in its desire to serve its patient population to the best of its ability. And we will continue to serve our patients in the surrounding community as long as there is a need for the kind of healthcare services that Norwegian American Hospital has to offer.

Norman R. Dahl,
Former Chairman of the Board of Trustees

Historic Timeline of the Hospital

The original hospital at the turn of the century

Main entrance of hospital lobby, circa 1928

Hospital gift shop

1885 The Norwegian Lutheran Tabitha Society of Chicago holds its first meeting.

1894 O.M. Torrison, chairman of the hospital board, lays the cornerstone for the new hospital in June.
■ Norwegian Lutheran Tabitha Hospital is dedicated in October.

1902 Dr. Christian Fenger, world renowned surgeon and pathologist and one of the first members of the Norwegian Hospital staff, dies.

1917 The hospital builds a 100-bed South Wing for $105,000 and changes its name to Norwegian American Hospital.

1929 The original 50-bed hospital building is razed, and the hospital builds a 130-room structure.

1930 A new 5-story building is erected, bringing bed capacity to 300, including 75 rooms for private patients.

1933 Trustees vote to place hospital into voluntary receivership.

1940 Woman's Auxiliary is formed.

1945 The Auxiliary opens a gift shop in the hospital lobby.

1946 Hospital survives financial crisis of the Depression and retires its debts.

1948 Hospital establishes several programs for the training of laboratory technicians, x-ray technicians, and nurse anesthetists.

New five-story Nurses' Home, under construction

1951 Woman's Auxiliary draws record-breaking 2,000 members and guests to the Grand Ballroom of the Stevens Hotel (now the Conrad Hilton Hotel).

1955 Agreement reached with Philippine Medical Placement Program for doctors seeking professional training in the United States.

1958 Hospital dedicates new five-story Nurses' Home built at estimated cost of $1 million.

1962 Norwegian American Hospital's School of Nursing, in existence since the hospital's opening, closes.

1968 Board of Trustees allocates $625,000 for expansion and remodeling. ■ Honor Roll, dedicated to memories of deceased medical staff members, is unveiled.

1969 75 years after its founding, the hospital is a block square and has a medical staff of 115 and 460 employees.

1971 New and expanded Radiology department is built at cost of $1 million.

1972 Hospital under siege with full-blown strike threatening closedown for 17 days but it prevails in the end.

Dr. Theodore Proud with the Hospital's Memorial Plaque

1981 New delivery room opens. Record 555 babies delivered in three months.

1982 Hospital contracts with National Medical Enterprises for the hospital operations. ■ Need to tighten hospital belt or to consider moving out. Hospital elects to stay to better serve its Northwest Side patients.

1984 ■ A Baby Fair and open house is held at the hospital to mark the opening of NAH's new nursery and recently remodeled pediatric care facilities. ■ New Hospital logo is adopted. ■ CAT Scanner is added to NAH's array of

Josepha, one of the many babies born in 1984, with parents Jesus and Bethsaida Gonzalez

imaging equipment, placing the hospital in foremost community ranks in area of Radiology.

■ Toll taken by diabetes annually is recognized as hospital opens Diabetes Management Center.

■ Norwegian American Hospital celebrates 90th year of medical care with year-long schedule of events commemorating its founding.

1985

Hospital launches beautification campaign. Main parking lot is completed. Numerous outside hospital banners are placed on lamp posts to identify the hospital and its location. ■ Health Works, industrial employee healthcare program, debuts to provide health services to 50 companies. In less than a year, more than 200 companies sign up for employee health care.

Beautification and landscaping received high priority

1986

New $2 million Labor/Delivery/ Recovery birthing area is completed; used by more than 400 couples in one year.

1989

NAH's 4,000 deliveries places it in top 10 hospitals in state for births. ■ Emergency Department sets new record in serving 23,000 patients.

1991

Hospital Board contracts for independent management. ■ New $5 million state of the art surgery opens. Includes 5 operating rooms. ■ Surgicenter, for patients requiring Same Day Surgery, debuts. ■ Century Physician Hospital Organization is formed to contract with HMOs for medical services.

Nurse assistant with Surgicenter patient

1992

Hospital records highest net income in 96 years of operation. ■ Completes major renovation of nursing units, pharmacy, support services.

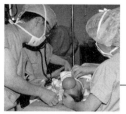

Maria Ugardo,
18-month old from
the Philippines,
undergoes surgery

Pradip Ghandi operating
blood count unit,
to determine presence
of infection

King Harald V
participates in the
Professional Medical
Building groundbreaking

1993   Hospital kicks off Centennial celebrating a
Century of Service with Viking Ball in October at
the Field Museum.

1994   Hospital outreach program reaches new humanitarian
goals with launching of medical missions to Bolivia,
Colombia, Peru, Philippines and Mexico. ■ As part of the
Centennial celebration, hospital launches year-long
panorama of events including free health screenings for
community residents, visits by Norway's Prime Minister,
Mrs. Gro Brundtland and her husband and by four-time
Olympic gold medalist, Norway's Johann Olav Koss.
■ Dedication of the Centennial Promenade as part of
the hospital's beautification plan. ■ Formation of the
hospital's own Lions Club, the Norwegian American
Hospital Century Lions Club. ■ Nine-year-old Marcelo
Fernandez of Bolivia, blind since birth with congenital
cataracts, undergoes sight-restoring surgery while a
toddler from the Philippines, Maria Ugardo, arrives at
Norwegian American for removal of face distorting
growth on her forehead, known as a meningocele.
■ Expansion of Emergency Room from 6 to 10 treatment
bays and upgrading to Comprehensive status opens door
to ambulance patients.

1995   Their Majesties King Harald V and Queen Sonja of Norway
visit Norwegian American Hospital and participate in
groundbreaking ceremony for a new Professional Medical
Building. Several months later Norman R. Dahl, Chairman
of the Board of Trustees, is conferred the Royal Norwegian
Order of Merit Knight First Class in recognition of his
humanitarian efforts in the medical mercy missions and
for his unwavering commitment to Norwegian American
Hospital and to the community it serves.

1997

Professional Medical Building

Dedication of new $11 million Norwegian American Professional Medical Building with 60,000 square feet for doctors' offices, and space for the new Women's Health Center as well as the Physician's Specialty Center. ■ Dedication of new Women's Health Center to address a wide range of women's healthcare needs and services in patient education, pregnancy prevention, life cycle changes, and other specialty programs. ■ Affiliation agreement is signed with Illinois Masonic Medical Center to provide tertiary services including nursery for critically ill infants, advanced cancer treatment, access to open heart (bypass) surgery and other services. ■ Five-year old Lawrence Baile, Filipino youngster born without a sex organ, is flown to Norwegian American Hospital to undergo the second phase of surgery for bladder neck reconstruction and closure of the open urethra. Surgery is performed by Dr. Casimir Firlit, Chairman of Pediatric Urology at Children's Memorial Hospital and Dr. Guillermo Gonzales, urologist on staff at Norwegian American Hospital. ■ Medical missions are conducted in Ecuador, Mexico and the Philippines.

1999

A few of the nurses and doctors participating in the 1999 Medical Mission to the Philippines are shown with boxes of medical supplies in the foreground. More than a thousand persons were treated at the clinic, sponsored by Norwegian American Hospital as part of the Mission. Clarence Nagelvoort, then hospital President and chief executive officer, is center in the photo.

Medical missions are conducted in the Dominican Republic and the Philippines. The Dominican Republic Mission proves timely, as many residents suffer through the devastating effects of Hurricane George. ■ Hospital announces plans to build new 5-story, 150-bed facility to replace old hospital. New $80 million facility to feature an expanded emergency room, in-patient psychiatric unit, addition of Magnetic Resonance Imaging equipment, enhanced cardiac catheterization laboratory to perform angiograms for treating severe heart blockage. ■ Existing hospital structure to be used as an assisted living facility for the elderly.

CHAPTER 1

The Beginnings

To understand the origins of Norwegian American Hospital, it is necessary to examine the forces shaping Chicago of the 1880s. The late Birger Osland, Board Chairman of the hospital during the 1930s, in his book: *A Long Pull from Stavanger*, describes the city as follows: "In 1888 Chicago was a bustling city of about eight hundred thousand inhabitants with railroads, factories, and stockyards, mud, smoke and smells...Of the Scandinavians, the Norwegians began to arrive in Chicago in the 1830s, but Swedish immigrants did not come in large numbers until much later."

It was a large, sprawling lusty city of Germans and Bohemians and Irish, Osland writes, but there were comparatively few Poles or Italians and few Negroes, and even fewer Norwegians.

Actually, Dr. Odd Lovoll, a professor at St. Olaf's College, places the first Norwegian immigrants in Chicago in 1836 when a small colony was started after they decided to remain in the city rather than to continue on to the Fox River, which had been previously settled. Dr. Lovoll describes the original settlement area north of the Chicago River, where it emptied into Lake Michigan, as "unhealthy" land known as the Sands.

The majority of the new settlers "squatted on canal ground, owning their primitive huts and shacks but not the ground they stood on..." To paint an even more realistic picture of the area, Lovoll writes, "In this area, at an appropriate distance from the commercial district....there emerged progressively cheap lodging houses, saloons, gambling dens, and brothels." Not exactly the most pleasant of areas in which to settle, to be sure.

In Lovoll's book, *A Century of Urban Life, The Norwegians in Chicago Before 1930*, the city was described by John Lewis Peyton, an Eastern lawyer, who arrived in Chicago in 1848, in this fashion: "The city is situated on both sides of the Chicago River, a sluggish, slimy stream too lazy to clean itself... There was no pavement, no macademized streets, no drainage and three thousand houses in which people lived..."

But Chicago even then had one big point in its favor, a plus factor which has spurred its growth over the decades: its strategic location at the mouth of the Chicago River, which Lovoll notes "was at the head of a portage waterway to Central Illinois and the Mississippi Valley...which through a canal could connect Lake Michigan to the Illinois River..." itself a tributary of the Mississippi. Such a canal, Lovoll observed, could create "a water route from the Great Lakes to the Gulf of Mexico." Despite its poor drainage and unhealthy location, the city continued to draw a steady stream of settlers.

What kept these early settlers in Chicago? "Chicago...as a port of entry for most Norwegian immigrants became for most...merely a dispersion point or at best a temporary home," writes Lovoll. "But for those who were without funds, and others who saw the chance to cash in on the booming city, Chicago offered hope and opportunity and they stayed on."

By 1850, Lovoll writes, Norwegians in the city numbered about 562. Many, whom he indicates would have preferred to settle in a rural community, were stranded in the city for lack of funds. Others remained in Chicago only long enough to earn enough money to purchase the farm they dreamed of.

For many the new Illinois Canal proved a great opportunity for jobs, and a Norwegian, Halstein Torrison, was in charge of hiring newly arrived Norwegians.

By 1845, the *Daily Democrat* could write, Lovoll notes, "the Norwegians are crowding to this country by hundreds ready to work on our canal."

What sort of a city was it? Writing in the Sons of Norway *VIKING* of December 1984, Lars Davidson Reque describes Chicago in 1839 as "the nastiest place you can imagine, nothing but a slimy marsh, with some miserable shanties here and there."

Compounding the problem was overcrowding so that epidemics could spread quickly. The 1849 cholera epidemic affected 332 Norwegians in a three-block area on the North Side, writes Reque, killing 44 before it was quelled.

Five years later, he writes, another cholera epidemic broke out in the city prompting one immigrant to write: "I enjoy living in Chicago but it is not pleasant to see black crepe on 17 doors within a block of your home."

Another Norwegian newcomer, arriving in 1847, reported to his friends in Norway, "If any nation ought to be praised for an unusual amount of illness, America certainly deserves the prize," Lovoll reports. This visitor found Chicago particularly bad. "With its crowded, filthy streets, drinking water, poor drainage, wet swamps and the polluted Chicago River, the city was...an unhealthy place. Deadly epidemics called forth efforts to improve the situation...but although progress was made...these efforts were inadequate."

The city presented a poor image to be sure, Lovoll writes. "With dogs roaming the streets, rotting animal carcasses, and underneath the wooden sidewalks, a numerous rat population."

Despite the horrendous living conditions and the hardships, settlers continued to arrive in Chicago. Soon the original settlers and others arriving in the decades to follow, in the '40s, '50s and '60s, were pushed from their original settlement to the sparsely settled area west of the North Branch of the Chicago River, writes Dr. Lovoll, concentrating on Milwaukee Avenue. By 1860 Chicago had grown solid to a half mile west of Halsted Street and as far north as Chicago Avenue, writes Lovoll, and it was no coincidence that this was the site of the new colony of Norwegian settlers.

During the '50s and '60s several large industries developed along the north bank of the river, according to Lovoll. These included the sprawling McCormick Reaper factory and a depot built by the Galena Railroad. While construction of railroad stations, factories and workshops furnished employment to many, they gave rise to workingmen's boardinghouses, and slums. But as residential areas along the river were converted to industrial use, residents were forced to move, partially in response to rising land values. Squatters were evicted, sometimes dramatically, Lovoll continues, as happened in a raid on the squalid Sands area, which Mayor Longworth ordered burned down shortly afterwards.

By the 1860s, Lovoll writes, more than 60 percent of all Norwegians in the city lived in that area and the colony flourished there for several decades until in the 1880s, they were pushed out of this settlement by the arrival of Poles, Polish Jews, Russian Jews and Italians. "Crowding in these dirty, smoky industrial river wards made it an undesirable district," Dr. Lovoll noted.

Many of these pioneer settlers were joined by the new immigrants arriving in a steady stream from Norway, and this time they established as their third and final colony in the city, the area a little further west, in Humboldt Park and Logan Square, Lovoll notes. Here, he says, they could set up their cheap frame homes and eke out a living.

Lovoll traces the growth of the Norwegian colony in Chicago from 18,000 in the 1880s, to 41,500 by 1900. By 1910 this number had risen only slightly to 47,200 Norwegians and that did not change much for the next decade, but by 1930, the number of Norwegians had risen to 55,948 making the Chicago settlement, the

A group of Norwegians are set to leave for Norway around 1902. If they planned to return or not is a question remaining unanswered.

third largest "Norwegian City" after Oslo and Bergen. These were the Golden Years, writes Dr. Lovoll of the period. The Chicago colony thus became a major cultural center within the entire national Norwegian ethnic population.

What did these Norwegian newcomers do for a living? According to Dr. Lovoll many became carpenters and tailors. Women found employment as domestics. And many Norwegians played a major role in shipping on the Great Lakes as seamen, captains and shipbuilders in the 1870s.

Like many other immigrant groups before them, the Norwegian settlers established mutual aid societies to help pay for burials and to support widows and children after their fathers and husbands had died. But for those unable to care for themselves because of illness, poverty, or old age, there was no help from these mutual aid societies, writes Dr. Lovoll. Such unfortunates were thrown on the good graces of various public and private charitable institutions.

Newcomers arriving from Norway would often arrive penniless or they would take sick and, as was the case of nearly all ethnic groups, they were helped by their countrymen who had come before them. Though such aid was well intentioned, it was scattered and unreliable to say the least, and often ineffective in providing for the care and treatment so desperately needed. It was agreed by virtually all in the Norwegian community, that there was a need for a better and more well balanced means of assisting Norwegian countrymen or their children in need and who were sick.

All that was needed at this point was some spark to get things moving. That spark was provided by a sermon given by Pastor A. Mortensen, a Norwegian seamen's pastor in Brooklyn, who had preached at several Chicago churches in October of 1885. In his speech Pastor Mortensen appealed to his audience and the Norwegian community to join forces to care for the sick. Many of these, he indicated, for lack of funds or other reasons, were left with little or no proper quarters or medical care of any kind. Shortly after this, at a mass meeting held in November of 1885, Mortensen's sermon moved a group of twelve women to found the Norwegian Lutheran Tabitha Society. This seemingly modest beginning set in motion a series of major movements in the community which led to the founding of two hospitals and at least one other well-established Norwegian institution: Norwegian American Hospital and Lutheran Deaconess Hospital (the forerunner of the present Lutheran General Hospital in Park Ridge) and the Lutheran Old People's Home in Norwood Park.

While this was happening, leading Norwegian men of the community, motivated by many of the same forces which had led the women to organize the Tabitha group, formed the Norwegian Benevolent Society to work for a Norwegian orphanage. Later, in 1888 after the Tabitha group's formation, the two groups merged and a Board of Trustees, consisting entirely of men, was formed. Dues for the Tabitha group were set at five cents a week; two thirds to go to urgent relief needs and one third to act as the nucleus of a fund to build the new hospital.

The inspired women then went to work with a new zeal. Through concerts, bazaars and picnics and any other means they could conceive, they collected funds for the sick and the needy. In addition, they made over old clothes at their meetings to use for children and others in need of clothing. For three years they continued in this manner. While much good was being done, the prospects for obtaining the money necessary to build a hospital were slim unless somehow or other they could get more support from the community at large.

Then in a meeting held at a local church in March of 1888, and attended by many of the leaders of the Norwegian community, it was decided to incorporate the society and the first board was named. It consisted as noted above of five leading men of the community, and a board of managers, the members of which were all women, was also elected.

With this new blood consisting of a group of able and successful businessmen behind it, the society was able to go about its fundraising goals with new zest. The aim was to build a new hospital at the earliest possible date. The new constitution gave the board new powers and one of its first actions was to purchase a site for $5,000 for the new hospital, on the ground where it now stands. It was only a block east of Humboldt Park, which was then, and still is, one of the most beautiful spots in the city. Since it was in the heart of the then Norwegian community, it was accessible to just about all of the Norwegian population.

At the first annual meeting of the society held in 1889, a new Board of Directors consisting now of five men and four women was installed. It was resolved to go ahead with the building of the new hospital, but it was also decided that the new Board would not take up deaconess work as part of its operation.

This created a major rift between those who wanted deaconess work to be a major part of the hospital, and those who wanted the lay element to predominate. As one writer put it, one group wanted to build a hospital to care for the sick; the other not only wanted this, but they also wanted to preach the gospel to the sick as well as visit them in their homes and have prayer meetings with them. So the original founders, who wanted to build and maintain a deaconess home, left and reorganized as the Original Norwegian Lutheran Tabitha Society.

Meanwhile according to historian Lovoll, the other group, which retained the name of the Norwegian Lutheran Tabitha Society, appealed to men of wealth and prominence in the Norwegian community saying: "It is astonishing that there has not yet been established a Norwegian hospital in Chicago, where there are so many helpless, sick, and poor....who struggle and toil in this world and who sooner or later must report to the public hospital or else die in the street."

Meanwhile six of the eight seceding directors of the "Original" Tabitha group, under the chairmanship of Pastor N.C. Brun of Bethlehem Church, secured a two-story house on Humboldt Street, in 1891, not far from the site of the proposed new hospital. They thus jumped the gun on the plans for a new hospital by the other group. Three sisters were brought in from Minneapolis to act as Deaconesses and by November 1892, some 53 patients had been cared for.

Patching up their differences the two Tabitha groups were again brought together, at least for the time being, Lovoll notes, and agreed to dissolve their respective groups to form a new organization to be known by the original name as the Norwegian Lutheran Tabitha Society.

Humbolt Park, located a few blocks from the hospital, as it appeared in 1885.

But in just a few months, in August, 1893, the original Tabitha structure on Humboldt Street was destroyed by fire. Now the two factions, once again united in their goals and activities, did everything they could to speed the completion of their dream, the construction of a substantial and suitable hospital building.

The united forces were able to raise considerable sums of money and gained broad support in the community. On June 3, 1894, the cornerstone of the new building was laid amid fitting ceremonies by O.M. Torrison, the president of the Board of Directors.

Charles Thisslew, a noted architect of Norwegian ancestry, was named architect. His instructions from the board were to build a "strong and serviceable structure." This he did and when the building was completed in the fall of 1894, Thisslew could say with considerable truth: "This is not a hospital, it is a fortress."

In October of 1894, the hospital was formally dedicated, with a large number of people on hand. It was an occasion of great joy, especially to the women of the society who, working with the clergy and the physicians, now saw before them a fine, up-to-date building – the embodiment of their dreams.

The original hospital at the turn of the century. It was described as a "fortress" by the architect, Charles Thisslew.

The first patient, admitted on December 3, 1894, was followed over the years by many thousands of patients. In fact the original building served for more than a generation, until it was torn down in 1929 to make room for a new wing of the rapidly expanding Norwegian American Hospital.

Beginning almost simultaneously with the opening of the new hospital and one of the factors which helped to speed the growth of the institution and which bolstered its reputation, was the start of a new nursing school for the hospital. When it opened in 1894, it had but two students enrolled for a two year course; but by 1930, the number of students had multiplied many times to 60 and its program had expanded to three years, in keeping with most of the hospital nursing programs then existent.

Nicolay Grevstad, the former Ambassador to Uruguay and the editor of the *Skandinaven*, notes in the history of the hospital that he was commissioned to write, that originally many of the applicants for nursing training were of Norwegian ancestry and had come from both Chicago and many communities out

Dr. Backus (left), Dr. Holmes (top center) and Miss Brekke (full white uniform) and staff (circa 1900).

of town. But by 1930, the year Grevstad wrote his story, the school was accepting applicants of all races and religious backgrounds and it had achieved in his words: "an enviable reputation for its thorough instruction and efficient training." Indeed many of its graduates had gone on to responsible and often high placed positions in other hospitals throughout the nation.

A good start had been made and the future looked promising.

Mary Hughes, a 1907 graduate of the hospital's nursing school, is a picture of loveliness in this shot. After graduation, she worked at the hospital for several years before marrying Ned Frost and moving to Cody, Wyoming, where she raised several sons and lived the rest of her life.

Members of the School of Nursing's Intermediate class gather for group shot in 1927.

CHAPTER 2

On the Way To Greatness

T he cost of the new structure was an unbelievable $37,000, all of which had been paid except for a $7,000 mortgage. The cost of a similar 50-bed hospital today would be approximately $13 million. Of course, the two structures would in no way be comparable because of the power lines, technological complexity and costly equipment needed for all new hospitals. Nevertheless, the new Norwegian Lutheran Tabitha Hospital was finally built, a beacon of hope for the Norwegian community.

Hospital as it appeared in 1925. Stairs leading to the original entranceway have been eliminated thus allowing direct entrance to the ground floor. Five-story South wing, immediately to the left of the main entrance, had just been built at a cost of $83,000.

But the good work accomplished by the women of the society could not stop once the hospital was built. That much was soon apparent. Funds were required for the hospital operation, for lighting and heat, for equipment, and for the staff.

At the time the hospital was built, the society had 340 members, 69 of them life members who had paid a one-time fee of $50 to be so designated and the balance regular members who paid twenty-five cents a week for dues. Through their various fundraising affairs, the women were able to raise about $700 a year to support the hospital operations.

The Tabitha Aid Society, a forerunner of the Norwegian Women's Auxiliary, formed several decades later, was a group of women interested in supporting the new hospital, who met every other week to make or provide surgical supplies, and other items needed in the hospital. What was unique about these ladies was that they were willing to help in any way they could. Thus if help was needed in the laundry, the kitchen or wherever, they were more than willing to give of themselves and their labor to do whatever had to be done. This willingness to help in any way was of critical importance especially during the early struggles of the hospital, when every penny raised was crucial. According to Grevstad, "much of the success of ... the hospital is due to their unflagging interest, their untiring efforts and their sacrifices of all kinds." Truly, their efforts were a labor of love.

Among the donors, who had each contributed $1,000 or more, was Victor F. Lawson, the renowned publisher of the *Chicago Daily News* and several other prominent Norwegian businessmen and leaders.

In his history of the hospital published in 1930 Grevstad described the hospital as follows:

"The rooms were small wards of three to six beds, besides private rooms, with the best modern ventilation. The halls were roomy and light. Elevators, electric lighting, sanitary plumbing, large bath rooms and other modern conveniences were provided. Two operating rooms, one for septic and one for antiseptic (germ free) surgery were equipped in accordance with the highest standards at that time, and a complete laboratory for histological and bacteriological work was the other essential of the equipment."

By today's standards the hospital would appear primitive, but by the standards of that day, it was state-of-the-art.

Besides serving the needs of the sick, the hospital also was to provide living quarters for the interns, nurses, the staff, and the elderly who needed living quarters – a lofty ideal, but one difficult to put into effect, as soon became apparent.

According to Bertram Jensenius, publisher of the *Viking*, Chicago's Norwegian newspaper, writing in September, 1960, "To provide a home for homeless aged people, the Tabitha Society assumed charge of nine old men and women, but it did not take long for the managers to realize that you cannot run both a hospital and an old people's home under one roof in a manner satisfactory to both. Another reason for taking this stand was the work already going on among the Norwegians in the city for the establishment of a home for the aged in Norwood Park."

So the Board decided that those already living at the hospital were to be cared for during their remaining days. Eventually, two of them were admitted to the Norwood Park Norwegian Home for Old People and one person was sent to the Danish Old People's Home. The others remained at the hospital until they passed away.

As noted above, the hospital was to provide living quarters not only for the sick, but various others as well, including interns, nurses, and staff. It was also to provide a storage place for supplies and equipment. Because of the rapid growth of the hospital and the need for additional space, an apartment building in the same block as the hospital was rented in 1902 as shelter for the nurses. But as so often happens, this modest space was quickly outgrown and in 1905 a Nurses Dormitory was built in the rear of the hospital. As might have been predicted, in a few years the dormitory was filled to capacity, and an apartment was rented nearby to provide some temporary relief until a larger, more permanent home could be provided.

The year, 1910, was a pivotal one in the hospital's history, one which Jensenius described as "the most important in the life of the hospital – next to 1894 when the first structure was erected, because the hospital trustees formulated the policies which once and for all removed the hospital from internal bickering and in time made it independent of the Norwegian colony...it paved the way for the hospital's integration into the community and the city of Chicago."

And here we come to one of the hospital's outstanding leaders, Dr. Marie Olsen, one of five women physicians then active in the hospital. Jensenius describes her as "a good-looking and Godfearing, friendly woman with a remarkable vision and the courage to tackle obstacles. Being herself a practicing doctor and a member of the board, she knew what the lack of clear cut policies could do to hamper the work of a hospital and cause management strife."

One of her first actions as Chairman of the Board was to introduce a motion which proposed that the hospital be strictly nonsectarian in policy and control. The motion was approved.

She realized that to invite doctors of other nationality groups to join the staff of the new hospital, it was essential to create an atmosphere which would induce such doctors to want to join the staff.

A plan was then evolved to give the staff home rule in managing its own internal affairs. As Grevstad put it: "The cordial relations existing between the medical staff and the business management have been a tower of strength in the development of the institution."

One of the amazing factors in the new hospital's development was the quality of the medical staff that it was able to attract, including some of the foremost men and women of medicine then practicing in Chicago. Certainly these would have to include Dr. Christian Fenger and Dr. Ludvig Hektoen, considered by many to be the most prominent men in Chicago medicine of the time. Complete profiles of both of these exceptional men of medicine appear in Exhibit 2 – Great Men and Women of Medicine of Norwegian American Hospital, pages 171-205.

Dr. Fenger was involved for many years with Norwegian American Hospital as a member of the board and the medical staff. In fact he served as chief surgeon following the long tenure of Dr. Karl Sandberg in that position.

Closely associated with Dr. Fenger and a man of international renown in his own right was Dr. Ludvig Hektoen, who was born on a farm in Wisconsin in 1863. Hektoen, who was 23 years Fenger's junior, subsequently completed his medical studies in 1887 as a graduate of the college of Physicians and Surgeons (later to become known as the University of Illinois Medical College). After taking first place in the intern's examination at Cook County Hospital, Hektoen returned to Chicago in 1888 where he came under the great influence of Dr. Fenger.

Hektoen exerted strong influence and leadership in the founding of Norwegian American Hospital, both as a member of the board of trustees, where he was a leader for more than thirty years, and in the establishment of a free tumor clinic in the hospital's early years. In his later years he collected several hundred of Dr. Fenger's medical articles and published them in two volumes entitled: "The Collected Works of Christian Fenger."

As a memorial to this great doctor, the Hektoen Institute at Cook County Hospital is named after him.

Another illustrious name in Chicago medicine during those formative years of the hospital was Dr. Karl M. Sandberg, born in Norway in 1855, who settled in Chicago in 1882. Here he established a very successful practice as an obstetrician and gynecologist. He was active in the formation of the Norwegian Lutheran Tabitha Hospital, later the Norwegian American Hospital, and was appointed surgeon-in-chief, a post he held for many years. He later served as president of the Scandinavian American Medical Society in 1892.

Yet another man of great stature in the Norwegian community and one of the founders of the Norwegian Lutheran Tabitha Hospital was Dr. Niles (Nils) Quales (Kvale in Norwegian). After serving in the Civil War as a veterinarian, Dr. Quales completed medical studies at Rush Medical College receiving the M.D. degree in 1866. He served as city physician in Chicago from 1868 to 1870 and besides being active on the staff of the then Norwegian Lutheran Tabitha Hospital for many years was later instrumental in the formation of Norwegian Lutheran Deaconess Home and Hospital. His wife, Carrie, was the cousin of the famous publisher of the *Chicago Daily News*, Victor Lawson. Dr. Quales later was on the medical staffs of both hospitals.

Another illustrious name in Chicago medicine of the time who early on became associated with the Norwegian Lutheran Tabitha Hospital, was Dr. Peter Bassoe, born in Drammen, Norway. Bassoe came to Chicago in 1893 and earned his medical degree at the College of Physicians and Surgeons in 1897. He went on to become world famous as a professor of neurology at Rush Medical College, and served on the Board of Directors of Norwegian American Hospital for many years until his death in November, 1945.

Equally prominent in stature of doctors on the staff of the hospital at the time was Anton Theodore Holmboe, born in Tromso, Norway, the son of Consul Conrad Holmboe. He was educated at the University of Oslo (then known as Kristiania), obtaining his degree in 1875. He then emigrated to America where he continued with his medical studies and was appointed mine surgeon for the West Republic

Mine in Michigan. He remained there until 1886, the year he was graduated from the College of Physicians and Surgeons in Chicago. For a few years, he assisted the famed Christian Fenger, but left to return to Norway in 1889 where he married Julie Opstad, whom he had met as a young man. After postgraduate studies in Berlin, he returned to Chicago where he started his practice and became one of the mainstays of the surgical staff at the then Lutheran Memorial Tabitha Hospital, following its founding in 1894.

Finally, to this list must be added Dr. Frederick Tice, associated for many years with Cook County Hospital and a professor of medicine at the University of Illinois College of Medicine. He, like many of these medical pioneers, added to his medical knowledge by study in Europe. As a consultant and private practitioner, he knew the problems of home and hospital, but he was happiest in the field of respiratory care and cardiac disease. His physical examinations, according to then hospital superintendent Kirk Besley, writing in the Summer 1958 *Lamp*, "were models of meticulous care and his loose leaf publication, "The Tice Practice of Medicine," so well known to medical students, was his method of constant revision as the pattern of disease and therapy changed. For more details on these historic medical leaders, see Exhibit 2, starting on page 171.

Interestingly enough, among the first to join the staff at the fledgling Tabitha Hospital were four young women, all of Norwegian extraction, in addition to the aforementioned Dr. Marie Olsen. Perhaps foremost among these and a distinguished physician in her own right was Dr. Helga Ruud. Dr. Ruud, a native of Kongsberg, Norway, studied medicine at Northwestern University, where she received her M.D. degree in 1897. A specialist in obstetrics-gynecology, Dr. Ruud taught at Northwestern from 1897 to 1901. From 1896 until she retired in 1943, she was on the staff at Norwegian American Hospital, one of the first hospitals in the city to open its doors to women physicians. (A complete profile on Dr. Ruud appears in Exhibit 2, page 180).

Another long-term member of the Norwegian American medical staff of great prominence both as a physician and for her activities in various Norwegian cultural and social groups was Dr. Ingeborg Rasmussen, who too received her M.D. degree from the Women's Medical School of Northwestern University in 1892. Shortly after the hospital's founding in 1894, she became affiliated with the medical staff where she remained in practice until she died in May of 1938.

The third woman physician to join the staff of the new hospital was Dr. Valborg Sogn, a native of Horten, Norway. In 1891 she matriculated at the Women's Medical School of Northwestern University, graduating with distinction in 1895. In 1902 she joined the medical staff at the then Norwegian Lutheran Tabitha Hospital as a gynecologist. She subsequently became a member of the board of directors and an instructor in the school of nursing before returning to Norway in 1910. She continued to practice medicine in Norway until she died in 1916.

Finally, there was Dr. Susan Ackermann, described in an article appearing in the March 1945 *Lamp* as, "one of the first women physicians admitted to the hospital staff, who had been a member of the staff for 35 years before she died in 1945." She was an honorary member of the Norwegian American Hospital Society and in 1930 had received the Cross of St. Olaw, one of Norway's highest honors, for her medical service rendered a young Norwegian sailor stricken on the Great Lakes.

Other profiles of some of the distinguished men and women of medicine who flocked to join the staff when it opened in 1893 are included in Exhibit 2.

With a splendid new hospital to its credit and an outstanding staff of doctors and board members, the hospital was well on its way to becoming one of the top ranking hospitals in Chicago at the time.

As a postscript to the hospital's founding and growth, it should be noted that the construction of the new Norwegian Lutheran Tabitha Hospital was not the end of the rift between the two groups involved in its creation – the Deaconess group and the more lay oriented group which was now in control.

In an article taken from "A History of the Norwegians in Illinois," the Rev. H. B. Kildahl writes that following the hospital's construction, "it became more and more evident that, while there was only one society, the two conflicting tendencies still existed..." As a result, many of the original members of the Tabitha Society broke away from the lay group and in September, 1896 were incorporated as the "Norwegian Lutheran Deaconess Society," with Dr. Quales as one of the three involved in the incorporation.

Several years later the society purchased four lots on the northwest corner of Haddon and Leavitt Streets, scarcely more than a mile from the new Norwegian Lutheran Tabitha Hospital. And by November, 1902, the new Lutheran Deaconess Hospital was completed and taken possession of by the Sisters and patients. So for 66 years until 1968, when Lutheran Deaconess Hospital was torn down on the site of the new St. Mary of Nazareth Hospital, the two hospitals existed side by side and many of the staff members of Norwegian American Hospital were also on the staff of Lutheran Deaconess Hospital.

Interestingly, Lutheran Deaconess Hospital was the predecessor of the Lutheran General Hospital of Park Ridge which was built after World War II and dedicated on Christmas of 1959. It became an outstanding institution in its own right.

CHAPTER 3

A Period of Boom and Expansion

The period from 1917, the first year of America's entrance into World War I, through 1930, was of great importance in the growth and expansion of the hospital. Under the then president of the board of trustees, Thorvald Johnson, the hospital launched a new building program which over the next 13 years would result in a complete rebuilding and modernization of the entire facility.

To speed the continued development of the hospital, the name was changed from Nor-

Members of class of 1916 take time out of their duties to pose for a group shot. Only students identified in the photo are, front row, Bella Olson, center, and Martha Moldenhauer, extreme right. Back row, Mrs. Rasmussen, center, Laura Madsen, second from the right, and Mrs. Ladendorf, extreme right.

wegian Tabitha Hospital Society to the Norwegian American Hospital Foundation, and the bylaws were rewritten to give the board broader powers, and the number of trustees increased from seven to nine.

Placed in charge of the building program, which would encompass the construction of several new additions over the entire period, was Olaus O. Krabol,

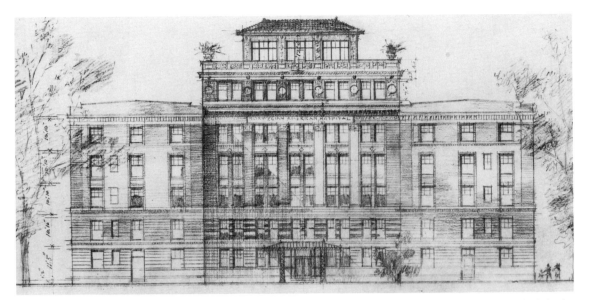

Artist's rendering of Giaver & Dinkelbert's new South wing, located immediately to the left of the main entrance on Francisco, in this drawing. The $85,000 structure added 100 patient rooms to the original capacity of 53 rooms.

as chairman of the building committee. First, the committee explored plans for building a new five-story south wing, to be built at a cost of $85,000.

Funds were raised by obtaining a mortgage from the Union Bank of Chicago for $85,000, but when this amount proved to be inadequate, Thorvald Johnson and Olaus Krabol each agreed to put up an additional $10,000 apiece.

The new structure, which contained rooms for 100 patients and a number of additional rooms for various other purposes, was the work of the firm of Giaver and Dinkelbert, engineers and architects.

That same year, a four-story building adjoining the original structure was completed for the nurses. Its main features consisted of music and reception rooms, light and airy bedrooms, among others.

Then in 1924 a new, up-to-date and ample power plant was built with a modern laundry on its second floor, at a total cost of $100,000, equipment included.

All this time, the board had been busy acquiring more and more property in the immediate vicinity – in the block bounded by Cortez, Francisco Avenue, Thomas and Richmond Streets.

Class of 1914, School of Nursing. Notice student names faintly outlined on their uniforms.

Several nurses at Norwegian American Hospital circa 1915. Only person identified in the photo is Gerda Rosendahl, second from the left, a 1913 graduate of the School of Nursing, who served in various capacities, including Director of the School of Nursing, from 1919 to 1935. She retired in 1962 with 44 years of service at the hospital, and was named Employee of the Year by the Chicago Hospital Council in 1962.

At the microscope. Nurse peers into the instrument in the new laboratory (circa 1923).

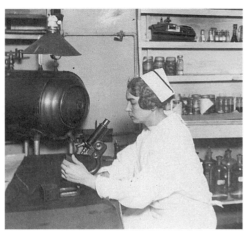

Next came another five-story building erected after a number of old homes on the west half of the property were torn down. This was an obstetrical building built at a cost of $300,000 including equipment. Among others it contained 104 beds and patient cribs. Its facilities included sewing and linen rooms on the first floor, as well as classrooms, and demonstration rooms.

The second and third floors housed rooms for twenty graduate nurses, 57 student nurses, and space for the office staff, the dietitian, the housekeeper and other staff members. The fourth and fifth floors were set aside for hospital use only.

Despite all of the additions, it remained yet to raze the original 50-bed hospital and to make room for a five-story, 130-patient room addition. The 130 patient rooms included 75 private rooms for patients with private baths and closets. There were also three operating rooms with up-to-date equipment and furniture;

Proudly holding newborn charges are several nurses in 1927.

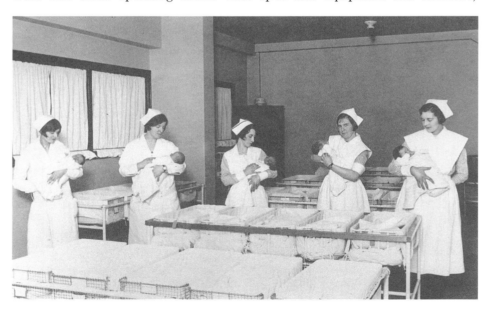

sterilizing rooms, doctors' and nurses' scrub rooms, toilets and baths, and locker facilities.

Five of the private rooms were completely furnished with funds supplied by board building chairman O.O. Krabol, and W.O. Johnson, Ole Gullicksen, long-time member and treasurer of the board, Birger Osland, about whom we will hear more later, and the H.D. Moreland Co.

The basement contained space for autopsies and for coroner's inquests, as well as storage space.

On the first floor was space for the business office, and the waiting room as well as offices for the superintendent and general offices, library, trustees room, three dining rooms for the doctors, nurses and office staff, a consultation room, a room for emergency operations, and finally a large kitchen

Typical nurse's station of the period.

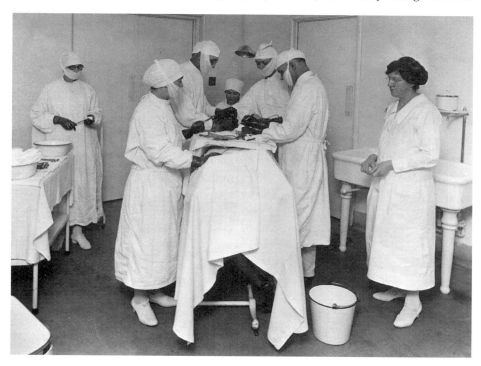

Hospital surgery in 1927.

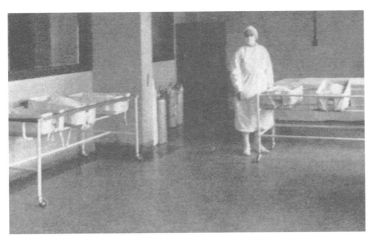

Isolation area of the nursery in the 1920s.

outfitted with modern and labor saving equipment, a diet kitchen and space for the dietitian, bakery and refrigerators.

The center section of the fifth floor was devoted strictly to a surgery suite, with a corridor for the public and a private corridor connecting the operating room with other facilities, and a waiting room for family and friends.

Other features of the new building: patient rooms equipped with nurses' signal system, telephones, outlets for lamps and electrical equipment and modern furnishings. Each floor had facilities for a doctor's call system, doctor's in and out system and a telechron

What the well-equipped hospital pharmacy looked like in the 1920s.

Group relaxing in the new nurse's lounge (circa 1927).

Hospital lobby, main entrance, circa 1928, was spacious and bright.

Typical four-bed ward, cheerful and well-ventilated.

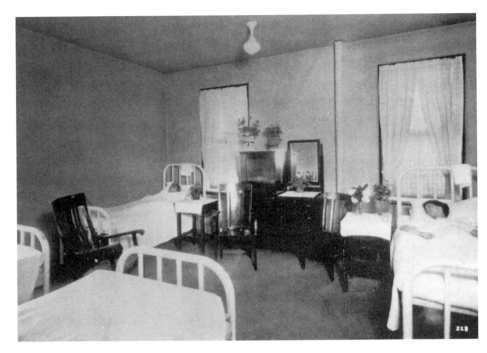

clock system with a master clock – in short, all of the features and enhancements to make the hospital as up-to-date and modern as any the city had at the time.

Perhaps most striking of all, the hospital now formed one complete city block bounded by Francisco Avenue, Cortez, Thomas and Richmond Streets, except for one comparatively small lot. To facilitate the flow of traffic in and out of the building, there were three passenger elevators, as well as a freight elevator and two dumb waiters.

With a total bed capacity of 300, including the 75 private rooms, Norwegian American Hospital now ranked among the largest and best equipped of not only all hospitals in Chicago but in the nation.

Total cost for this entire building complex was an estimated $850,000 of which $430,000 was financed through first-mortgage bonds.

All of this planning and expansion was accomplished under the leadership of Olaus O. Krabol, first as chairman of the building committee, and later as the president of the board of trustees.

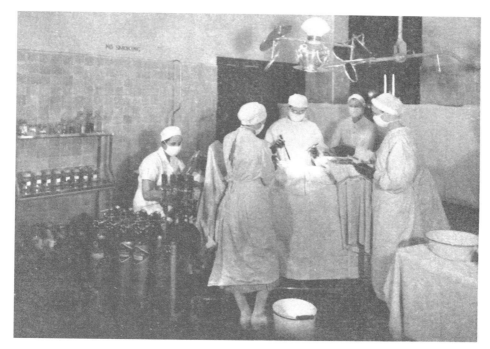

Surgery: The start of a laporatomy.

The building expansion is only part of the story. Yet another indicator of how the hospital was growing is seen in the modification and modernization of equipment and space within the new buildings.

For example, the operating rooms were among the first to be changed. First, the entire complement of equipment was replaced; new operating room tables, the most modern of the period, were installed as well as instruments, lighting and so forth to provide a surgery that could offer the latest in efficiency and safety.

With the addition of the new building, the entire old building was set apart for obstetrics and nursery. The entire fifth floor was devoted to delivery rooms, sterilizing rooms, work rooms and waiting rooms for mothers about to go into delivery. Not the least noteworthy of the section was a large, sunny and well ventilated nursery with thirty infant cribs, and a new incubator.

X-ray facilities were not to be outdone at the facility. Starting with a small room equipped with an apparatus costing $500, the department was enlarged with a new set of equipment including a fluoroscope enabling the diagnostician to set

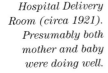

Hospital Delivery Room (circa 1921). Presumably both mother and baby were doing well.

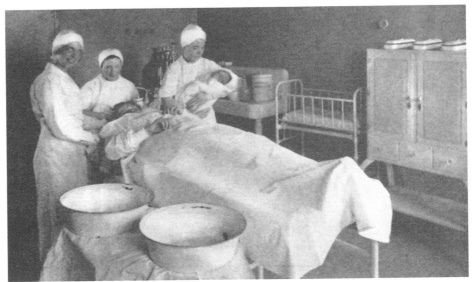

fractures and often enabling the x-ray department head to determine if surgery was called for or not.

The pathology laboratory, at first equipped with a barely adequate supply of equipment, was expanded to become in the words of one writer, "a model of efficiency."

In 1921 the services of a well-qualified pathologist was engaged as well as three technicians.

Yet another measure of the hospital's growth was the increase in the size of the medical staff. In 1923, just 30 years after the opening of the new facility, the attending staff numbered 50 in charge of the actual work of the hospital – giving daily clinics, demonstrating and conferring regarding cases of special interest, and arranging lectures by instructors on subjects of interest for the entire medical staff.

By 1930 the medical staff numbered 85, both men and women, comprised primarily of physicians of Norwegian or Scandinavian descent in keeping with the nature of the institution at the time. The staff was headed by Dr. F. E. Thornton, President; Dr. E.P. Wright, Vice President; Dr. Ralph H. Warden, longtime chief of radiology, Secretary, and Dr. C. Gunderson, Treasurer.

Before leaving this chapter, one further important change should be noted – the organization of a non-profit trust: The Norwegian American Hospital

Foundation, with the trustees given full power to do all required to "establish, maintain and operate the hospital...in the service of humanity and not for profit to the trust or the trustees individually." And the name of the hospital was changed once again: this time to Norwegian American Hospital, which was to remain its name down through the current times.

Under the new structure, the hospital was to be governed by nine trustees with the stated purpose to operate a hospital in the "service of mankind" and not for profit to either the trust or the trustees individually. The trust was given clear and unconditional control of all phases of the hospital's operation, including the school of nursing, and in taking whatever steps were judged necessary to operate most effectively. The trustees were to serve without any compensation and any vacancies were to be filled by the remaining trustees.

Named as trustees of the Foundation were:

Olaus O. Krabol, President,
Chairman of the Colonial Chair Co.

Walter O. Johnson, Vice President,
Head of T. Johnson Co., coopers

Ole Gullicksen, Treasurer,
President, Churchill Cabinet Co.

Andrew Hummeland, Secretary
Counsel, attorney

Oscar H. Haugan, Vice Chairman of the Board
Foreman – State National Bank of Chicago

Adolph H. Nordahl
Nordahl & Olson, jewelers

Dr. Marie A. Olsen

Birger Osland
Birger Osland & Co., investment bankers

John M. Pedersen
John M. Pedersen Mortuary

In charge of the entire hospital employee staff was Jennie E. Madsen, R.N.

As was true of the medical staff, the nursing complement was almost entirely of Norwegian or Scandinavian origin. This included the Superintendent of Nurses, Gerda J. Rosendahl, who remained on staff for several decades; surgery supervisor, Gena Johnson; supervisor of obstetrics, Randi Gimse; nursing supervisor Jennie Abrahamson, and Laboratory Technicians, Huldah Johnson and Carlotta Anderson. However, according to *Vinland*'s editor, Jensenius, the Norwegian influence did not hold true of the students, roughly half of whom had what he termed "strange sounding" names. But as he put it, "It assuredly makes no difference whether a nurse be of Norwegian or Polish descent. But it does show the end of the times...the (beginning of the) Americanization...the melting pot." The increasingly diverse nature of the hospital's constituency is seen in a 1928 report of patients' nationalities which noted that of the 5,776 total patients that year, 4,577 were of American background and the balance came from some 38 countries, including Hungary, Iceland, Ireland, Serbia, Turkey, Mexico, Latvia, and Palestine. But of the foreign patients admitted, the largest number by far were from Norway, with 192 patients admitted that year.

All of this vast expansion of facilities had been accomplished through the vision and dedication of the hospital's hardworking President, Olaus O. Krabol. Total cost of all of these improvements was estimated at $850,000, with an estimated indebtedness of nearly $500,000. This might under ordinary times give pause and some concern, but times were good. It was the era of prosperity of the Coolidge administration and the indicators were for clear sailing. The hospital was in good shape, or so it appeared.

CHAPTER 4

The Storm Clouds Gather

B ut it would have taken a person with the foresight of Solomon to see the storm clouds that were gathering on the horizon. Just a few months after the change in the hospital structure, the Stock Market Crash occurred on July 1, 1929, ushering in a period of economic decline and hardship throughout the country the likes of which the country had never seen in modern times. Dozens of hospitals, which like Norwegian American had expanded, now were caught in an economic vise between the cost of operating the hospital and precipitous declines in patients and income. Many had to go out of business.

Norwegian American Hospital was no exception and by 1930 a number of belt tightening actions were taken to help get out from underneath the tremendous debt the hospital had assumed. Several Trustees, including President Krabol, were pressed to offer their own funds, secured by 6 percent bearing loans. For instance, in May, of 1931 President Krabol advanced the hospital $4,200 of his own funds to meet interest payments. And in May of the year preceding, 1930, the hospital had only $4,000 on hand to pay interest which amounted to $8,200. The $4,200 required to meet the balance of interest due was offered by Trustee Ole Gullicksen.

In January, President Krabol reported that a note of $3,000 payable to the Union Bank of Chicago had been renewed with the understanding that it would be repaid at the cost of $500 per month. He further reported that through negotiation he had been able to reduce the cost of milk and cream bought from Bowman Dairy Co. by $50 and $60 a month. He also obtained a slight saving in the compensation allowed student nurses amounting to several dollars a month.

When a $50,000 note held by Foreman-State National Bank became due, a subcommittee of the board was able to obtain a 60-day extension on the note.

If this was not enough, Secretary Andrew Hummeland reported that he had obtained a tax exemption for some property adjacent to the hospital for the years 1930 and 1931. Finally, an across the board cut in the salaries of all employees from top to bottom was put into effect. All of this action was taken in a period of a year or two in 1930 and 1931 to try to stem the tide which threatened to engulf the hospital.

A finance subcommittee headed by Birger Osland had suggested approaching nurses, alumnae, doctors and members of the society for contributions to the hospital. Despite all of this, the hospital still looked as though it might go under.

Then on June 20, 1936, the man under whose leadership the hospital had undergone such a complete expansion and revamping of facilities, Olaus Krabol, suddenly died. Little wonder why a scant 10 days later the Board of Trustees passed a special resolution expressing its gratitude for all that Krabol had done for the hospital. It read as follows:

"Olaus O. Krabol will be remembered in years to come not only as an outstanding Chicago businessman but as an exponent of unselfish service in our community.

"He gave unstintingly of his time and energy to the management of one of the great civic undertakings in our city, the Norwegian American Hospital, Inc., serving as President of its Board of Trustees for twenty years until his death on June 20, 1936.

"While his colleagues on the Board of Trustees acknowledge his exceptional qualifications as a successful business leader, they particularly appreciate his unflagging interest and unceasing labor on behalf of the Norwegian American Hospital, which, under his wise leadership, has grown from a modest beginning to its present high rank amongst the hospitals of our city.

"The trustees of Norwegian American Hospital, Inc. feel a profound sense of loss in the death of Mr. Krabol and it is hereby resolved that this expression of our deep sorrow at the loss of a great personality be spread upon the records of the Norwegian American Hospital, Inc. and that an engrossed copy be sent to Mr. Krabol's family."

Later it was decided that a copy of the resolution would be hung in the Trustees room at the hospital.

But with or without Mr. Krabol, the hospital was still confronted with the battle to get out from underneath the sea of debts which continued to threaten its existence.

Fortunately, Norwegian American Hospital had the right man in the right place – Birger Osland. In 1923, Osland, a well known investment banker, and self-made man, was invited to join the Board by Olaus Krabol. Upon Krabol's death in June, 1936, Osland was elected President. (A complete biography of Birger Osland appears on pages 181-183, Section 2). At the time the Board of Trustees consisted of 14 including the previously mentioned Dr. Peter Bassoe and Dr. Ludvig Hektoen, who continued on the Board until his death in 1951.

Typical of the caliber of leadership of the Trustees of the period was John M. Pedersen, owner of a local funeral home, who had served on the Board virtually from its founding in 1894. His long years of devoted service ended on October 13, 1937 with his death. Afterwards the Board, in appreciation of Pedersen's long and dedicated service to the hospital passed the following resolution:

"The career of John M. Pedersen, who died on October 13, 1937, in his 66th year, is another reassuring illustration of the fine success which the individual can achieve out of the opportunities that modern society affords.

"He was born in Kristiansund, Norway, and had the advantage of a good education. He selected to emigrate to the United States of America, and his choice proved well made. He was one of the list of public-spirited Norwegian Americans who constitute so strong a force for good in Chicago and particularly among his own countrymen. He was active in all good causes and a liberal contributor to all. Modest, genial, sympathetic and responsible, he was one of the most lovable of men."

All the time however, the tremendous debt remaining still unpaid of the previous decade loomed over the hospital threatening to choke off its very existence.

The last of the new buildings to be dedicated for hospital use was the five story, 130-bed unit referred to in Chapter 4, which replaced the original hospital building. Included in the new structure were three operating rooms, a reception area, business office, library, dining room, kitchen and three passenger elevators.

The principal speaker at that time was Dr. Hugh S. Cumming, surgeon general of the United States. Just a scant two years later, Osland writes in his book: *A Long Pull From Stavanger*, "Revenues had fallen off so much, the board of trustees was forced to place the hospital in voluntary receivership.

"Some of the trustees, individually donated funds to insure payment in full of interest when due. But when the next semiannual interest date came around the situation was still worse....

"Most hospitals in Chicago had difficulties during this depression. Several were placed in receiverships and some closed, never to open again..."

In 1933, writes Jensenius, "... the Board of Trustees placed the hospital in voluntary receivership, and the Circuit Court of Cook County appointed a Bondholder's Committee, which cooperated with the trustees in starting the uphill road to economic recovery and financial stability."

And uphill it was. With hospital occupancy dropping dangerously low, the hospital, under Osland's leadership, went on a strict austerity drive. The medical staff, nursing staff and all hospital employees were asked for contributions, wages were cut to the bone, jobs were merged. In the words of the hospital publication, *The Lamp*, "By strict fiscal policies, careful planning and perseverance, the Board of Trustees fought the hurricane. Not only was the institution saved from financial ruin, but in 1948 it could proudly announce that the $500,000 had been paid in full..."

Despite the hard times, the medical staff according to its president, Dr. Harold Sofield, a well-known orthopedic surgeon, had still managed to attract more doctors to the staff than in any other of the preceding ten years and now numbered 130.

Meanwhile, as is inevitable, changing times and changing neighborhood ethnic composition had changed the makeup of the hospital, at least from the standpoint of the medical staff. Writing in his book, *A Long Pull from Stavanger*, Osland wrote that in 1945: "The hospital is located in a neighborhood once almost exclusively Norwegian; now few of them are living there. The medical staff of the hospital has ninety-five members; seventeen are of Scandinavian origin, including two of Swedish and two of Danish descent. The other members of the staff are largely of old American stock with some German Americans, some Polish

Americans, and some Italian Americans." Slowly, but surely, the medical staff at least was changing its ethnic composition, from one almost exclusively Norwegian to one composed of various ethnic elements. But the Board of Trustees, however, remained strictly Norwegian.

Looking back on those not too distant days it seems incredible to modern day readers accustomed to mushrooming hospital rates and services that in February of 1937 the rate for rooms in the new section of the hospital was only $6 per day; while the room rate in the hospital's older section was a mere $5 a day. This in comparison to modern day hospital rates which are currently approaching several hundred dollars per day. Even so, proof of the hospital's prominence in the Norwegian community of that day is a statement in Osland's book: *A Long Pull from Stavanger* that of the ten or so leading Norwegian charities of the period, the most valuable by far was Norwegian American Hospital with an estimated net worth at the time of $1,012,163, followed by Lutheran Deaconess Hospital with an estimated net worth of $834,054.

Writing in the October 6, 1960 issue of *Vinland*, Osland paid tribute to his close associate and colleague on the Board, Elmer Abrahamson, for many years the Board Secretary....noting, "It is only fair to mention that the legal steps taken in this difficult situation, when a mortgaged debt of $500,000 fell due, were planned and guided by ...Mr. Abrahamson, who was then and still is attorney and secretary of the hospital Board of Trustees...." Mr. Abrahamson passed away in December, 1989.

The next president, who was in office from 1947 to 1953, was Isak B. Faleide, and his administration was one of recovery. Under his leadership the hospital gradually pulled out of the Depression as it again went forward on the right track. Faleide was a native Norwegian, who after emigrating to the United States in 1902, established the Faleide Engineering Co., a firm which was engaged in building industrial plants, flour mills, cement mills, grain elevators and so forth throughout the country. For a complete profile on Mr. Faleide, see Exhibit 2, page 184.

What was Faleide proudest of in his stewardship of the hospital? Again, Editor Jensenius quotes him in *Vinland* as saying: "What I am proud of is that in ten years every penny of the depression debt of $500,000 was paid off." With the money the hospital was able to set aside, it built a sparkling new lobby, with an extended front and a new gift shop and coffee nook, the products of the newly installed Women's Auxiliary.

Relatively modest hospital admitting office as it appeared in the early '40s.

In 1940, while the Board was still led by Birger Osland, the dedicated hospital women, many of them daughters of the original Tabitha Society members – took a very important step in the hospital's continued operations. Joined with the wives of trustees and the medical staff, they organized the Women's Auxiliary in 1940, and one of their first steps was the opening of a lobby gift shop in 1945. Annual card parties soon were a feature of the new Auxiliary, and these were held regularly at the Swedish Club, at the Graemere Hotel in Garfield Park and at the Drake Hotel.

One of the Auxiliary's most popular and helpful acts was the creation of a free circulating library for all patients. Of great natural interest was the increasingly busy obstetrical department, so in 1944, as a Father's Day goodwill gesture, the Auxiliary completely redecorated and refurnished the father's waiting room. Yet another Auxiliary program helped to finance the nursing education of deserving students.

As these service and social events grew in popularity and support, the membership continued to grow until 1951 – a banner year – saw more than 2,000 members and guests attracted to the Grand Ballroom of the Stevens Hotel (now the Conrad Hilton).

In time, benefit luncheons and fashion shows became highly popular both as fundraisers and as social events. Later an annual dinner dance was added to the Auxiliary's list of attractions and in time became one of the group's most popular events.

Over the past 59 years, the Auxiliary, now known as the Women's Board, has contributed well over $500,000 toward the purchase of needed equipment or improvements. In 1998, for instance, through the annual Christmas holiday Bake Sale, a Valentine's Day Flower Sale, and a December jewelry sale, the Women's Board raised more than $7,000.

In addition, the group realized more than $20,000 through the sale of fixtures of the old gift shop, which was discontinued. Most of the revenue from these various events went to the support and establishment of a new Women's Health Center (see Chapter 10, page 91).

The special niche occupied by the Women's Auxiliary is seen in a letter written to the then president of the Auxiliary, Mrs. Ellen Pedersen, by the then hospital administrator Richard W. Sellers in 1969 which says in part, "Your loyalty, dedication, talent and skills – not to mention hard work – have in no small measure contributed to the success of the hospital."

Hospital gift shop, which opened in November 1945, as it appeared about a year later, crammed with notions and gift items. It was one of the first projects of the newly chartered Women's Auxiliary.

Nursing School Class of 1940 presents a sprightly appearance. Numbering 23 students, class was one of the largest in Nursing School history.

In these and in various other activities, the Women's Auxiliary was established to serve as a role model in supporting services and programs to help the hospital meet its commitment to the community, and this remains the primary objective of the Women's Board, as it is known today.

Two other important programs undertaken during the administration of Board President Faleide are worthy of mention. The first, which arose in the years following World War II, was a dire shortage of nurses which the hospital faced. In fact, Jensenius writes in *Vinland*, "the shortage had reached the point where the Board felt that they had to shut down a section of the hospital, so as to care for patients."

To solve the problem Faleide succeeded, with the assistance of the American Scandinavian Foundation, to work out a program enabling Norwegian nurses to finish their training in the United States at Norwegian American Hospital.

Later the program was broadened to include doctors, who served both as interns and residents in completing their postgraduate training at Norwegian American Hospital.

At one point, Faleide estimated, there were as many as 28 Norwegian nurses working in the hospital, 16 as trainees. Many of these, having completed their 18 months of training, returned to Norway and later came back to America, where they became permanent citizens, working primarily as nurses, and many of these as nurses at Norwegian American Hospital.

In furtherance of its objectives as a training ground for nurses, the School of Nursing in 1948 could boast at the time the largest class in its 54-year history of 13. Also of great interest was the fact that the hospital had established several other programs which were flourishing at the time for the training of hospital technicians and laboratory assistants. Included were training programs for a school of x-ray technicians, a school for medical technologists and a newly formed program for the training of nurse anesthetists. Applications for all three training programs were being received from all over the country according to the *Lamp* in 1945.

In addition, the *Lamp* noted, six rotating internships were offered annually as well as residencies in surgery. The internships and residencies were fully approved by the respective specialty boards and by the American Medical Association.

Heading into the 1950s things were looking up indeed for the little hospital located near Humboldt Park.

Profiles of the two great leaders referred to in this chapter: Birger Osland and Isak Faleide appear in Exhibit 2, pages 181-185.

CHAPTER 5

Completion of Another Dream – a New Nurses' Home

For most of the 1940s the hospital rolled along as best as it could. With World War II intervening, the pages of the *Lamp* were filled with items about various members of the medical staff, the trustees, and the general staff who were in the armed forces fighting for Uncle Sam, contributing to the end of the war in one way or the other.

A contingent of NAH staff members on duty in the South Pacific during World War II. Major Harold Sofield, a distinguished orthopedic surgeon and president of the medical staff in 1930, is shown at the extreme right.

The March 1945 issue of the *Lamp*, for instance, contained several items on members of the medical staff who were in the service including: Lt. Commander G.B. Fauley, stationed at the University of Chicago, who was commended for his article in the December 30, 1944 issue of the *Journal of the American Medical Association*, on "The Use of Penicillin in the treatment of Peritonitis," and one Lt. Junior grade P.C. Irvine, stationed on an LST somewhere in New Guinea, who had taken part in the invasion of Leyte in the Philippines; and Lt. Commander J.S. Verhaag, sending his congratulations to the *Lamp* on the news it carried of the hospital; also Captain J.E. Caliendo, who had seen action in France, Belgium, Luxembourg and Holland, and finally on Lt. Col. M. Lichtenstein, Assistant Professor of Surgery at Northwestern University, who had received a citation and bronze star for meritorious service in support of combat operations in Italy with the 5th Army. No doubt about it, Norwegian American Hospital was doing its share and then some to speed the war effort.

In a report issued by then Honorary Chairman Birger Osland on the occasion of the Hospital's 60th Anniversary in 1954, he commented on several changes that had been made to add to the hospital's attractiveness and effectiveness: "...a new attractive main entrance and lobby was built, the office space modernized and enlarged, additional room and facilities provided on the first floor for the X-ray department."

The Seufert Memorial Library was a favorite place of study for many nursing students.

He further noted: "The gift shop in the lobby, operated by the Women's Auxiliary...was enlarged and a brand new coffee shop, also operated by the Women's Auxiliary, was installed."

"On the second floor," he commented, "the Drug Store benefited by greatly enlarged quarters as did the Sterilization Department. Additional doctors' examining rooms were added."

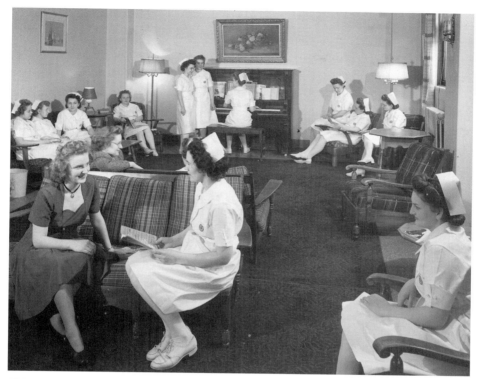

But the nursing student's lounge with its piano and comfortable sofas was the place for rest and relaxation.

Classroom lectures occupied a good part of the nursing student's day during the 1940s.

He further noted that the Medical Library and the Physical Medicine Department had found new and enlarged quarters on the second floor.

Finally, he observed, "the building...now covered the entire block bounded by Francisco Avenue, Thomas, Cortez and Richmond Streets."

The medical staff, Osland's report continued, "consisted of 100 physicians, surgeons and specialists in the various branches of medical science, while the nursing staff consisted of 126 graduate nurses, including 25 at Norwegian American Hospital temporarily from European hospitals for the purpose of studying American hospital practices."

Hospital sun porch was a favorite place for relaxation for patients for many years. It eventually was demolished when the new surgery unit was built in 1995.

In concluding he praised the hospital School of Nursing, noting that "since 1896 fifty-seven classes totaling 753 students had been graduated. The present enrollment consists of 52 students," he added.

With World War II ended and the hospital finances in good shape, the board of trustees could once again focus their attentions on the future. Going back to 1930, preliminary estimates had been obtained for building a new Nurses' Home. But hard times and the financial problems confronting the hospital put all such plans for a new home on hold. The dream, however, was not forgotten. It was kept alive over the years and indeed the need for a new Nurses' Home became increasingly obvious with the passage of time. But by 1945, the building fund established for this purpose stood at a mere $11,000. By 1954, however, it had increased to the sum of $140,000. Then in 1955, the Ford Foundation notified the Board of Trustees of a grant in the amount of $91,200, and this was followed by a generous contribution from the medical staff of $150,000. At last it became apparent that the cherished dream of many years could now become a reality.

New five-story Nurses' Home built at a cost of $1 million is seen under construction in 1957. New building, designed by architects Schmidt, Garden & Erikson, provided quarters for 60 student nurses as well as facilities for 66 additional patients.

On April 5, 1957, the many hospital friends and associates gathered for the historic groundbreaking ceremonies for the new home, led by the then Board President Elmer Hansen.

By June, 1958 the new addition, designed by architects Schmidt, Garden and Erikson, was completed at an estimated cost of $1 million. Besides providing residence space for 60 student nurses on the first, second and third floors, it contained facilities for 66 patients on the fourth and fifth floors. The additional beds brought to 250 the total number of beds available for patient care, and with the new facility, the total value of the hospital figured conservatively stood at $5 million.

The new Nurses' Home was indeed a welcome addition. It was equipped with complete tiled bathroom facilities, built in closets and dressers, and a mixture of attractive color schemes surrounding the handsome furnishings.

For the patients, the addition offered the fine feature of being able to rest on the most modern electrically operated beds with matching dressers and patient tables. Indeed nothing was left undone to make the patients' hospital stay as pleasant and comfortable as could be.

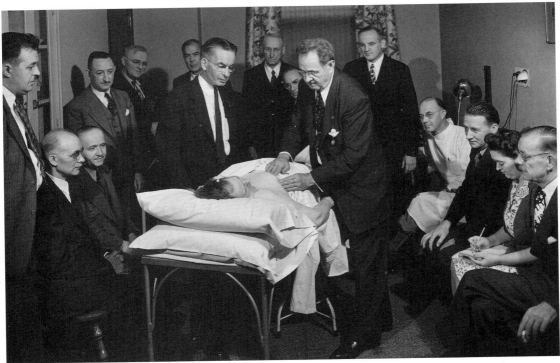

Clinics in various areas of medicine were held weekly during the 1940s. Here, staff is gathered around patient as doctor examines her as part of the tumor clinic.

In addition, the new facility offered game rooms, TV rooms, reception rooms, lounges and a large volleyball and badminton court for the student nurses in their residential areas. Finally, the library was combined with that of the medical staff making available a vast additional amount of current nursing and medical literature. Since its beginning in 1894, the Norwegian American Hospital's nursing school had seen more than 800 nurses receive their training and graduated.

With all of this new building reaching a high point, the hospital still maintained a superlative medical staff. Profiles of just a few of these distinguished men and women are to be found in Exhibit 2, including Drs. Manuel Lichtenstein, Anton Jensen and James P. Ahstrom, starting on pages 171. Of special note was the fact that more than 25 percent of the medical staff had been actively connected with the hospital for 25 years, a record few other institutions could match. But increasingly, perhaps mirroring the changing complexion of the ethnic mix of the surrounding community, the staff began to include a growing number of non-Norwegian sounding names.

And so, the hospital was set for the boom years which followed.

CHAPTER 6

Into the 1960s and 1970s: a Period of Expansion and Retrenchment

B
y and large the period of the 1960s and 1970s was one of continued growth and prosperity – both of the hospital itself and in the services offered and the number of patients treated.

For several years after the dedication of the new Nurses' Home in 1957, the hospital continued on an even keel. The next major expansion and rehabilitation of the facilities was undertaken in 1960 and 1961. At that time two of the operating rooms were modernized, and the entire north half of the fifth floor was completely remodeled to offer as modern an obstetrical facility as could be for the time. The new department featured an obstetrics service which combined maternity, delivery and recovery sections. A similar renovation followed on the fourth floor to provide a more attractive and larger space for the pediatrics department.

Then under the stewardship of John Hanson, president of the Board, a sizeable expansion and remodeling program involving the expenditure of more than $625,000, was approved. It provided for the

Hospital building as it appeared in 1969 with new entrance facade. The year marked the hospital's 75th anniversary.

complete renovation of three floors of the hospital, expanded the space for laboratory facilities and services, and made other long-needed departmental improvements.

The prime benefactor of this new expansion program, the laboratory, moved into its new space, doubling its former size, in early 1970. The new quarters offered brand new furnishings, a much needed air-conditioning system and the latest in interior design.

Of the 42 new beds scheduled for the third and fourth floors of the hospital, 33 were set aside for general medical and surgical use and 9 for an expansion of the current Intensive Care Unit. The installation of these beds brought the hospital's total capacity at the time to 264 beds.

Very much a part of the 1969-70 expansion was a doubling of the size allocated to Inhalation Therapy and major improvements in air conditioning and other features of the Pharmacy and Physical Therapy Departments. In the words of Administrator Sellers: "...it was only the first phase of our long-range plan to provide modern facilities and the best possible care for our patients." Indeed, Sellers' words proved to be prophetic. Much more was to come including complete renovations of the obstetrics department and the facilities for the care and treatment of young children, as well as completely new and expanded surgery and emergency room departments. These further expansions and renovations will be discussed in the chapters to come.

For now no history of Norwegian American Hospital would be complete without a word on the hospital's long-standing record as a community hospital with a strong teaching and training component.

We have already seen the enviable record recorded by the School of Nursing, which grew and developed along with the hospital. It was always an integral part of the hospital's operations. Unfortunately, that historic record of achievement came to an end in 1962, when the school was closed following a resolution of the American Nurses Association calling for increased emphasis on the four-year nursing program at colleges and universities throughout the country, and the granting of the bachelor of science degree in nursing. As a result, many of the thousand or so hospital nursing programs, even those so well established as that of Norwegian American Hospital, were on the decline. Even so, the School of Nursing had blazed a truly remarkable record in its nearly seven decades of existence, with more than 927 graduates completing its rigorous training program.

Many of these graduates went on to distinguished careers in nursing not only at Norwegian American Hospital but at hospitals and medical centers throughout the nation and indeed throughout the world.

But the closing of the School of Nursing was not the final chapter in the hospital's educational training programs. We have already referred to the hospital's excellent training program to help fully educated nurses from Norway to advance their professional skills. This program was developed with the assistance of the American Scandinavian Foundation.

In the area of medical training, a program calling for the training of resident physicians was overwhelmingly approved by the medical staff in 1965. However, the passage of the years saw an ever-increasing emphasis being placed on specialization, which called for a good deal more expense and a greater number of years to train residents in various specialties – often three to five years over and beyond a year of internship.

As a result, the smaller community hospitals had to rely increasingly on recruitment of foreign doctors for internships and residencies. We have already seen in Chapter 6, the expansion of the nursing program to nurses from Scandinavia who were seeking to perfect their training through the help and sponsorship of the American Scandinavian Foundation. Subsequently the program was expanded to include doctors too.

For several years, this program saw the recruitment of numerous Scandinavian physicians seeking opportunities for postgraduate studies. Eventually however the program gradually declined primarily because Scandinavian physicians training in the United States for a year or two of postgraduate studies would lose seniority in their homelands, where the shortage of doctors was critical. This is seen by a rundown on the residents studying at Norwegian American Hospital in 1952. According to the Spring 1952 *Lamp*, these numbered three from Denmark and three from Norway, and one each from Canada and Hungary, and two each from Latvia and Poland.

But by 1954, a new agreement had been reached with the Philippine Medical Placement Program, an organization working out of Manila, serving as a clearing house for Filipinos seeking additional professional training in the United States.

The program, which had the blessing of the American Medical Association, was developed along the lines of the National Intern Matching Plan prevailing among medical schools. Reflecting this new agreement, four interns from the Philippines came to Norwegian American in July 1955 as well as a young doctor from Norway, thus bringing to eleven the total number of physicians on the hospital house staff.

By 1969 the shortage of qualified graduates of American medical school graduates reached the point where most of the internships and residencies in non-affiliated (community) hospitals were filled by foreign medical graduates.

As Dr. R. B. Robins, the hospital's director of graduate medical education, put it: "Most of the American medical school graduates stay in medical school affiliated hospitals for internships and residencies." He noted that the leading countries supplying foreign medical graduates for residencies and internships in non-affiliated, community hospitals were the Philippines, India, Korea, and Thailand.

By 1972, two years after Dr. George T. Murphy had taken over as director of medical education, the house staff was composed of 13 interns, three surgical residents and eight general practice residents, nearly all of them foreign medical graduates, and this was the trend throughout the 1960s and the 1970s. The training, however, was outstanding, as Dr. Murphy noted in his department report of 1972. He noted that "monthly meetings and reviews were held for clinical pathology conferences, and equal lectures and conferences in internal medicine, general practice, obstetrics and gynecology and tumor conferences."

In addition films of special interest were shown as time permitted, and special guest lectureships were arranged and supported by the medical staff, while clinical bedside rounds were held two to three times weekly. "These exercises are extremely important..." Dr. Murphy wrote, "since many of our young people have not been taught the value of learning at the bedside during rounds...when both old and new clinical skills and recent scientific methods can be applied in a broad approach to the problem of the patient."

Gazing at the names of deceased members honored by the hospital's Memorial plaque in a 1968 photo is Dr. Theodore Proud. The name of Christian Fenger, world-famous pathologist and an early member of the hospital staff, occupies the upper lefthand tablet on the Memorial.

Complete profiles on the lives of Dr. Murphy as well as other physicians active at the time: Dr. Helen Button, Dr. Isadore Isoe, and Dr. Rasmus Harr, are contained on pages 192-200.

But in the areas of patients served and treated, the hospital continued to reach new records in almost every area during the 1960s and through the mid '70s. This can be seen by the steady progression from the 7,796 patients admitted in 1967 through the 14,694 admitted in 1975. This same rise in other services can be seen virtually all the way down the line. For instance, in 1967, the number of babies born was just over a thousand; but by 1975, more than 2,000 babies were born at Norwegian American Hospital; the number of emergency room visits went from 3,643 in 1967 to 8,215 in 1975; radiology examinations went from 17,377 in 1967 to 42,999 in 1975 and laboratory procedures increased from 106,453 in 1967 to 383,970. These same increases in hospital statistics were recorded in the number of outpatient visits, emergency room visits, and days of care. As an interesting corollary, the number of hospital employees jumped from 422 in 1967 to 649 in 1975.

Quaint costumes were the order of the evening at the hospital dinner dance co-hosted by the Women's Auxiliary in 1970. Left to right are Ellen Pedersen, Auxiliary President attired in patriotic motif, Betty Hughes, lei-bedecked Hawaiian and Solveig Haslerud, in gypsy costume.

Colorfully garbed members of the Women's Auxiliary at statue of Viking explorer Leif Eriksen in Humboldt Park. Ladies dressed in Norwegian outfits as a preliminary to the 1971 annual Viking Ball, are Mrs. Jacqueline Moe, left, Auxiliary President, 1975-77 and Mrs. Julie Highland, wife of the late Irving Highland, President of the hospital Board of Trustees in 1971.

Several Norwegian American Hospital veterans are seen in this photo taken in the early 1970s. Left to right are Dr. Donald H. Crabb, family practitioner, Mrs. Gudrun Hagsrom, R.N., Mrs. Helen Johnson, R.N. and Dr. Lars Andrew Dolan, for many years the hospital medical director.

From 1975 on, however, the hospital began to see a slight decline in various hospital statistics which continued through the end of the 1970s. For instance the number of patients admitted declined from 14,694 in 1975 to 14,248 in 1977; babies born dropped from 2,009 in 1975 to 1,731 in 1977; and the number of surgeries declined from 74,431 in 1975 to 72,360 in 1977 and this held true of almost every other measure of hospital activity and service.

Even so, a hospital showing such a steady increase in patients admitted for most of the period, and in various services rendered must show a corresponding increase in equipment, space and facilities and in personnel employed if it is to handle the increased load. And this was soon evidenced at Norwegian American Hospital in almost every area of the hospital. In the laboratory for instance in 1971, while Dr. Aaron Learner was the chief pathologist, (see profile in Exhibit 2, page 201) several new and highly complex pieces of equipment were installed. The first, known as an autoanalyzer, tests blood for traces of kidney disease while at the same time analyzing blood glucose and nitrogen. According to Dr. Learner, the autoanalyzer made for greater efficiency and productivity in a field where personnel are often in short supply.

In addition, a newly installed pulmonary function tester was soon put to good use by Dr. Everildes Yarzagaray. The unit analyzed both maximal breathing capacity – the amount of air a patient can inhale and exhale as fast and deep as they can – and vital capacity, or the amount of air a patient can exhale after a deep breath.

Its primary use, Dr. Yarzagaray explained, was to provide quick and early detection of such pulmonary diseases as emphysema, bronchitis, asthma, lung embolism and other lung diseases.

Then in Spring of 1975, the hospital's new and expanded radiology department was ready except for a few finishing touches. Built at a cost approaching $1 million, the new facility was additional evidence of the hospital's willingness to serve the healthcare needs of inner city residents with the very finest of equipment and facilities.

According to Dr. Raymond DesRosiers, then head of Radiology, the newly refurbished and expanded department featured lively color schemes throughout, indirect lighting and vinyl covered walls. The primary feature was four major examining rooms for fluorographic, radiographic and other x-ray examinations and for photographing nuclear medicine studies of various body organs.

Additional space was set aside for private offices, waiting rooms, files, reception and dressing areas, a doctor's viewing area and a separate suite for urological procedures.

The department renovation and expansion was necessitated by the increased load of radiographic examinations that the department had to process in 1974. Dr. DesRosiers noted that at that time the departmental staff of 22 technicians and administrative personnel conducted 326,222 diagnostic examinations of 21,778 hospital patients per year.

But undoubtedly the major building and renovation project undertaken was a $2 million reconstruction and remodeling project which got underway in July, 1975.

Essentially the project called for a complete revamping of three floors – the basement, the first and second floors. The interior courtyard, at first and second floor levels, was also scheduled for enclosure.

Besides calling for major revisions in the hospital's plumbing, heating, ventilating, air conditioning and temperature control systems, the work included a consolidation of administrative offices and the installation of several new pieces of equipment including an autopsy table, morgue refrigerator, whirlpool bath for physical therapy and a vacuum sterilizer.

To soften the impact on patients and staff, always a major consideration, contractors were required to do everything possible to reduce noise and dust, by installing such equipment as dust partitions, rubbish chutes, and noise buffers. They were also obligated to perform all duties without any interruptions in normal hospital functioning.

The story of Norwegian American Hospital would be virtually complete were it not for two very special events which occurred in the early and mid-'70s which had great impact on the hospital's functioning. The first of these events, a fullblown strike, threatened for 17 unforgettable days a complete shutdown of the hospital. The story is described in the Summer 1972 *Lamp* which we quote: "It was definitely a climactic moment in a confrontation that had begun during the early morning hours of April 19 when pickets suddenly appeared at all entrances of the hospital and refused to permit the removal of garbage or the delivery of supplies, including such vital materials as blood, oxygen, food, infant formula and pharmaceuticals."

"The hospital and its patients, to all intents and purposes, was in a state of siege."

"What happened from this point is etched in the memory of all who were involved. The struggle to load and remove mountains of garbage...the smuggling in by doctors and staff of badly needed foodstuffs, medicines and other supplies... the continual harassment, threats and acts of vandalism..." and so the article ran on.

"Throughout the confrontation," the story continues, "the public was on our side."

"In using hospital patients as hostages," *Chicago Today* editorialized, "the strikers have adopted tactics that would be called an atrocity in wartime," but with the return to normal activities, the story continues, "we can look back on the siege of '72 with more calm and understanding. One thing is certain. The confrontation has strengthened our belief that hospitals filled with innocent and helpless patients are incompatible with powerful unions...we can't see where any outside third party – union or otherwise – can add either to our compassion for our fellow man, or our ability to serve him at the time of greatest need."

The strike was undertaken by HELP, the Teamsters Union affiliate that had been attempting to unionize the hospital. But after 17 days of the siege, a ballot was taken. The result: of the 188 employees who had cast valid ballots, 98 had voted against the union and 90 in favor. The strike had been defeated and was now a matter of history.

The other major event, of a much happier nature, was the week-long visit of King Olav V of Norway to commemorate the 150th anniversary of the arrival of Norwegian settlers to America.

Highlights of the King's stay included a visit to the Lutheran Memorial Church on North Kedzie Boulevard, the only church in Chicago where services are still conducted in Norwegian, a concert by the Chicago Symphony Orchestra featuring Norwegian music, and a banquet at the Marriott Hotel with approximately 1,000 guests including Governor Dan Walker, Ambassador Sommerfelt of Norway and members of the Norwegian-American Sesquicentennial Immigration Commission.

In his talk the King noted that "even though the first settlers were more interested in farming than in developing a city, the Norwegian community has left strong imprints on the city through its churches and hospitals, through its educational institutions and organizations, clubs, and newspapers."

The King knighted hospital trustees Irving Highland and Dr. Rasmus Harr for their work in the Norwegian community here and for Mr Highland's aid to Norwegians during World War II.

As the 1970s came to an end, there was evidence that although the hospital had expanded and been of ever-increasing service to its now largely Latino constituents, at least through 1975, times were changing and the hospital was finding it increasingly harder to make ends meet in the years that followed. Clearly, several hard decisions would have to be made about the future, and these will be described in Chapter 8.

Profiles of some of the distinguished medical men and women on the medical staff at Norwegian American during this period, including Dr. Bernard Kleppel and Dr. August Daro, are contained in Exhibit 2, pages 202-205.

CHAPTER 7

Some Hard Decisions Are Faced

As has been seen in Chapter 6, the 1970s started out well at Norwegian American Hospital, but by the mid-'70s, affairs took a turn for the worse in almost every area – especially in the all important area of net revenues. A study of net income, or operating revenues, showed that from 1979 through 1982, hospital revenues had declined from almost one and a half million dollars to three quarters of a million and in nearly every area of hospital operations, patient admissions, length of hospital stays, surgical procedures, number of babies delivered – the figures had either declined or remained fairly level. Only in emergency room visits had there been a sharp increase in statistics, from 11,356 in 1976 to 23,500 in 1993.

The problem was primarily the heavy load of what has been termed "disproportionate" patients – patients who were either on Medicaid (public aid), Medicare (for those over 65) and patients completely without insurance. In Norwegian American's case, in 1988 for instance, the figures showed that the total of such "disproportionate" patients was about 66 percent, a figure which has remained fairly constant over the years and in the decade preceding 1988. Because of the low repayment schedules paid for patients in this category, hospitals such as Norwegian American typically receive in essence only 47 cents of every dollar of patient charges and the hospital's operating income of only $340,000 in 1988 was a vast drop from the operating income of $3,081,000 registered in 1986.

Clearly, the hospital was caught in a crunch which threatened its very existence. And it was not alone. From 1983 through 1988, 10 Chicago area hospitals had closed primarily for economic reasons. Several had closed from 1985 to 1988, including St. Anne's Hospital on the West Side, reportedly the largest hospital to close until that time. Another hospital that had closed in the early 1980s was Walther Memorial, just west of Norwegian American, on the other side of Humboldt Park.

Norwegian American was hardly in an enviable position. Like many other hospitals in the inner city, it had been buffeted for the past decade by the rising tides of change in the healthcare industry. Between 1983 and 1986, occupancy in Chicago hospitals as a whole declined from 80 percent to 59.1 percent. And the entire repayment process, which had been in place since the advent of Medicare in the mid-'60s, was swept away by a new system – Diagnostic Related Groups (DRG's), where hospitals were paid a fixed fee or rate based on the patient's diagnosis. If the hospital's cost remained lower than the DRG rate, it came out alright; but if costs were greater than the amount allocated under the DRG, the hospital had to make up the difference out of its own funds.

As the hospital Chairman, Norman R. Dahl, put it in his report of 1987, several years after the hospital had turned the corner in its struggle to survive, "the hospital was losing money and lacked management leadership. We either had to tighten our belt or consider moving out of the neighborhood." Several hospitals caught in the same predicament, had already chosen to move out to the suburbs where they could serve a more affluent patient population, one more likely to have adequate hospitalization coverage.

At Norwegian American the answer was an overwhelming vote to stay on to serve the needs of residents of the Humboldt Park, West Town and Greater Northwest Sides, when the matter came up for a decision in the early 1980s. In this area, which the hospital had served since its founding in 1894, the healthcare needs of the basically Latino population were disproportionately great.

The next question which the Board of Trustees had to grapple with was how to cut costs and to increase revenues within the limitations imposed by the hospital's overwhelmingly "disproportionate" population, comprised of better than 66 percent Medicare, Medicaid and non-insured.

After considerable soul searching and discussion, the hospital decided to turn over the day-to-day management of the hospital to National Medical Enterprises, a private management company with an excellent track record in running troubled hospitals, hospitals beset with problems similar to those facing Norwegian American.

In 1982 National Medical Enterprises sent William (Bill) Leyhe to serve as president and chief executive officer of the hospital. A young, yet capable executive (he was only 32 when he came to Norwegian American), Leyhe soon had the hospital on the right track by adding new revenue producing departments, (which will be enumerated in the pages that follow) and by immediately instituting a belt-tightening control in all areas of hospital operations.

Among the hospital's achievements in Leyhe's four-year administration; the cash position was significantly improved, from $1.6 million in 1982 to in excess of $11 million in 1986. Income from surgeries performed, which was $300,000 in 1980, averaged in excess of $3 million for each year from 1984 on.

Norwegian American's obstetrics department, with more than 2,000 deliveries per year, became one of the most active in the Chicago area and vaulted to more than 4,000 deliveries in 1989 to put the hospital among the top ten in the state in the number of babies delivered.

Following a complete renovation of the pediatrics department, which will be described in the pages to come, the hospital experienced a 30 percent increase in patient volume in that area from 1982 to 1986.

In the emergency room, Emergency Consultants, Inc. a professional management group, was employed to provide full-time health care in that area and volume increased almost immediately during 1985 to more than 1,100 patients a month.

Worth every minute of anxiety and stress associated with birth is baby daughter, Elizabeth, born to father, Lidio Guerrero and Mom, Juana in 1989. Baby was one of 4,500 infants born at the hospital that year, making Norwegian American second highest in live births among all Illinois hospitals.

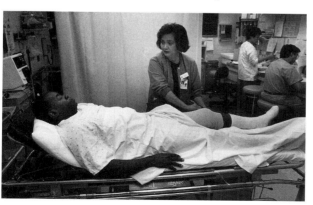

One of the record-breaking 23,000 patients treated in the Emergency Room in 1989 is seen with Unit Coordinator Norma Dela Cruz. Because of the tremendous volume of patients treated in the ER, the hospital opened the new million dollar Emergency Room in 1993, which more than doubled the emergency room's capacity.

Dr. Daniel Alcasid, medical director of Health Works, hospital's occupational health program, treats patient for arm fracture. She is one of thousands of employees of community industrial plants and offices participating in the program.

During 1985 the hospital focused on occupational health and in less than one year, more than 200 companies employing some 8,000 workers were members of the NAH Health Works program, initiated at the hospital that same year. Under this new program, employees of subscribing companies who are injured on the job through burns, lacerations, fractures, etc. are treated at the hospital and returned to work afterward.

At the same time the hospital sought to improve its visibility in the community by installing new signs and banners over major routes in the area, and beautifying the neighborhood with shrubs, grass and trees.

Such were a few of the innovations and new services launched under Leyhe's leadership. But even with this expansion, tight controls were put into place. As a result the break-even point (the number of patients the hospital had to admit to break even) was lowered from 160 patients a day in 1981 to 124 in 1983 and 108 in 1985.

Sidewalk repair was one of many beautification projects the hospital launched in the 1980s.

Landscaping of areas surrounding the hospital was one of several major projects undertaken during 1986.

Mary DeJesus, Hospital Service Aide, was one of many employees who planted more than 1,000 plants in the hospital picnic area in 1986.

Hard at work at Bargain Boutique on North Milwaukee Avenue operated by the Woman's Auxiliary for many years through the '80s are these ladies. Only persons identified are Florence Keller, second from the right, and Bernice Widmar, head of volunteers at the extreme left.

All of these new services and innovations will be described in the pages that follow. Leyhe's achievements were recognized not only by those in authority at Norwegian American Hospital, but by his own company as well. And on January 11, 1986, he left NAH to assume a post as vice president of operations for the entire western region of National Medical Enterprises.

All smiles is Hanna Nodland, RN, as she poses in colorful garb she wore for the Norwegian Day parade in 1988.

His successor was Michael Sussman, a 20-year veteran in healthcare who had been associated with National Medical Enterprises for six years before switching to Brim & Associates, another management company in healthcare, in 1987. Sussman continued the remarkable recovery the hospital had enjoyed under Leyhe's leadership with other innovative and highly successful programs of his own, during his four-year leadership stint at Norwegian American, from 1987 to 1990.

Rear entrance to the building (Richmond Street) as it appeared in 1989.

Once these hard-core decisions had been made, the hospital embarked on a new program of expansion and improvement in 1984 which touched upon every floor of the hospital. Two of these major projects are especially noteworthy – a new special care nursery offering state-of-the-art facilities for the newborn and a completely renovated and expanded pediatrics unit.

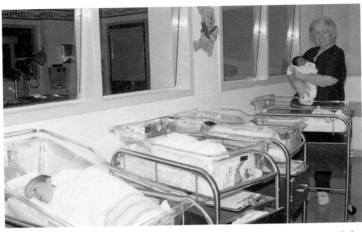

The decision to go ahead with the new nursery, at a cost of approximately $1.4 million, was based primarily on the fact that deliveries at NAH had increased in the previous four years. Also, with a surrounding population in the Humboldt Park/West Town area with 28 live births per thousand residents, the community had the highest birth rate in the city, nearly twice that of Chicago and the rest of the nation of 14.8 births per thousand.

Holding one of her precious newborns is Joan Paulov, head nurse of the hospital nursery for 28 years, who recently retired after 41 years of service at Norwegian American.

The new nursery of 5,000 square feet of floor space featured a family approach to infant care emphasizing sophisticated technology. Featured were computer controlled incubators, a computerized system for measuring oxygen levels of newborns without taking blood samples, an electric pressure monitor, a glaucometer to measure sugar levels within two seconds, other monitors recording heart and respiration rates, and specially designed digital scales that can track weight within a tenth of an ounce. Offered on a round-the-clock basis was a neonatal medical service to handle any emergencies and to monitor newborns classified as high risk.

Smiling brightly with her newborn daughter, Sabrina, is Marcia Lomax, one of thousands of mothers who have their babies at Norwegian American every year.

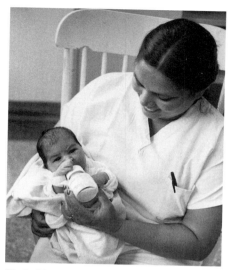

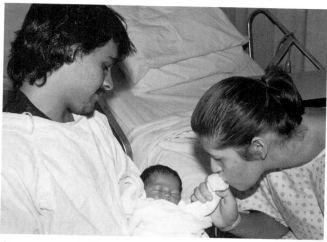

Sit-in Mommy for newborn is Joginder Kaler, RN, as she feeds little one in photo taken in 1984. At the time babies in the nursery were fed six times in 24 hours.

Shown gazing fondly at their newborn daughter, Josepha, are Jesus and Bethsaida Gonzalez. Baby was born September 5, 1984.

According to neonatologist Dr. Joseph Villalona, who started at Norwegian American in 1986, 7 per cent of the babies born at the hospital are classified as high risk. Why? Inadequate medical care is often the prime cause with the hospital seeing more and more mothers who have had little or no prenatal care, and as a result, the babies are premature. Other causes of high risk babies: diabetes, hypertension, and drug addiction. But no matter what the cause, Norwegian American had a team of neonatologists, pediatricians and registered nurses specially trained to work in the hospital's Special Care Nursery or the Intermediate Care Nursery. Both nurseries care for newborns who are sick or premature, but in the Intermediate Care Nursery, the babies have stabilized.

"These babies need assistance with breathing," said Dr. Villalona. "We are buying time until the babies' lungs mature. Once babies can breathe on their own, they are allowed to go home."

Quite often survival requires a balance between care and tenderness and technology. "Here at Norwegian American, we try to find that special balance," said Dr. Villalona. "Because the babies need touching and encouragement, we urge

No stranger to the joys and sorrows of newborns who are premature or otherwise require special care is Dr. Joseph Villalona, neonatologist at Norwegian American, shown as he monitors infant in the Special Care Nursery in 1988.

parents to visit any time of day or night, in order to somehow break through any technological barriers that may exist when the baby is attached to a respirator."

"But at the same time, the technology – respirators, incubators, radiant warmers and oxygen monitors – enable babies who weigh as little as two pounds to survive."

But the battle doesn't end when the parents take their little ones home. Once a month, the hospital holds a High Risk Clinic. Dr. Villalona monitors the baby's progress and advises the mother on postnatal care.

The new facility provides for 30 Level I bassinets and six Level II bassinets for infants requiring intensive care.

The year 1984 also saw the 32-bed Pediatrics Department undergo extensive remodeling and renovation to provide more space and medical equipment for the short-term treatment of critically ill children and to handle a predicted increase in pediatric age patients. Intended to make hospital stays more pleasant for both the children and their parents, the new facility featured an intermediate care room for acutely ill children, isolation rooms for those with contagious diseases, and video equipment that monitors the condition of youngsters occupying these special rooms.

To make the new Pediatrics unit even more attractive and homey, it featured child-size furniture, rooms painted in bright colors and a playroom featuring toys selected to emphasize the family centered aspect of the unit. To further stress the family aspect, parents were encouraged to sleep overnight in their child's room on special fold-out lounge chairs or through use of a nearby parents' lounge open 24 hours a day.

The year further saw the installation of the hospital's new CAT (Computerized Axial Tomography) Scanner. Ray DesRosiers, M.D., then chairman of the Radiology Department, observed that the CAT Scanner "by combining rapid small dose x-rays with computerized enhancement of the resulting picture virtually eliminates the need for exploratory surgery." This coupled with the Department's use of ultrasound, nuclear medicine, and other diagnostic imaging equipment, placed NAH in the front ranks of community hospitals equipped to image the body and its various organs and systems.

The year also saw the installation of a new sign at Sacramento Boulevard and Humboldt Park as well as the planting of new flowers, shrubs and trees on the hospital campus as part of a new beautification program.

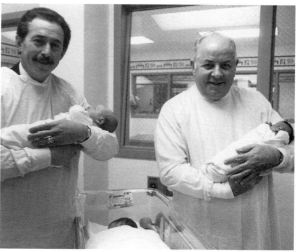

It's smiles all around as Norman R. Dahl, former Chairman of the Board (right) and Michael H. Sussman, then President and CEO, are shown with newborn charges in the hospital nursery in 1988.

Further, the year witnessed, under the leadership of Dr. Eduardo Barriuso, the initiation of a $2 million remodeling, expansion and upgrading of the hospital's Obstetrics department to expand its 1,700 square feet of floor space to 5,000 square feet, nearly tripling the available space for delivery of babies. The new unit, complete with the latest in equipment and facilities to make birth a beautiful and pleasant process, further underscored the commitment of the hospital to the more than 2,000 babies born at the hospital every year.

For the first time at NAH, mothers entering the delivery process, were able to start the labor process, give birth, and recover in the same room. Aimed at duplicating the comfort and atmosphere of the home, the new LDR (Labor, Delivery and Recovery) suites were intended to make delivery a pleasant and rewarding exper-

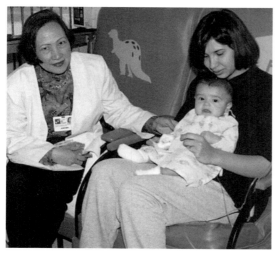

Holding 4-1/2 month old Fabiola, is her mother, Veronica Hernandez, seen with Anita Horwath, Clinical Nurse Manager, Pediatrics.

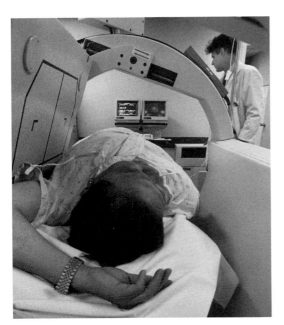

Performing lung scan on patient is Radiology's Peter Cutera. Shot taken in 1991 features the department's new nuclear scanner known as SPECT. Scan was performed immediately after patient completed a stress test in which she was given thallium, a radioisotope useful in imaging various parts of the body.

ience for the mothers. Supporting the closed doors of the LDR rooms, was the latest in equipment available in the event of complications. Besides the five LDR rooms, with the homelike settings, there were two traditional delivery rooms for use in more complicated deliveries.

The unit also included three traditional labor rooms designed for first time mothers who usually face lengthy labor cycles. When the expectant mother is ready to deliver, she is either moved into a traditional delivery unit or the home-like Labor Delivery room.

According to the Hospital Administrator in charge at the time, Michael Sussman: "The birthing experience is special. We want to make the birth a family-oriented event where the mother and child can experience those early moments of bonding in a setting that is warm and comfortable."

"Family members can participate in the joy of a new life in a room that looks and feels like their home, yet has all the latest medical technology," he added.

One of the most innovative of the new programs started under former administrator Leyhe's leadership was Health Works occupational health program begun in 1985. (See page 58.)

Included in the services offered were new employee physicals, drug screening and treatment of work-incurred injuries such as fractures, eye injuries and burns. In short, Health Works offered a complete variety of health services to keep employees on the job and functioning when they are injured or disabled.

A growing part of the program is drug screening, in which hospital personnel screen employees on an individual or group basis for evidence of drugs or alcohol or both. Besides this, the various screening services offered to communities for, among others, diabetes, blood pressure, and eye problems – are offered to participating companies as weil.

An example of benefits offered to subscribing companies was a breast screening made available in 1998 to company employees at a discounted price of $50 per screening. To promote the screening, the hospital distributed promotional material to companies advising the availability of the screening, and listing dates, times, and places for the screening.

According to Janina Nieves, R.N., B.S.N., former Director of Ambulatory Services, and coordinator of the Health Works program, the screenings offered are part of a Wellness component, aimed at keeping company employees healthy and on the job. Besides the screenings for such disabilities as high blood pressure, diabetes, and so forth, the hospital offers flu shots for subscribing companies' employees. Currently, says Ms. Nieves, 500-600 patients are being seen at the hospital each month under Health Works, which represents a considerable increase over the previous year. And the outlook for even greater participation is excellent as more and more companies enroll in the program.

Further evidence of Health Works attractiveness was its widespread growth in only a few years. By 1992 ten new companies were added to the more than 633 already enrolled in the program for a total of 393,409 employees registered in the program and an additional 24,344 employees and their families participating in the Health Works Plus program. The latter program offers participating employees and their families physician visits, diagnostic testing, pharmacy, dental and vision care. A total of 5,852 patients were treated under the Health Works program in 1992.

In 1987 following the completion of the new LDR suite, the hospital saw a record-breaking 2,416 babies born. That figure in turn was to be later surpassed in 1989 when 4,200 births were recorded at the hospital, placing NAH in the top ten hospitals in the state in the number of births.

That same year, 1987, in recognition of the increased toll being taken by diabetes on the American public – it is the third leading cause of death by disease contributing to seven percent of all deaths in the United States every year – the hospital opened the Diabetes Management Center. The department offered a "Center for Excellence" through its 21-bed inpatient service and through a comprehensive outpatient service.

The objectives of the Diabetes Management Center are to assist the diabetic in the management of diabetes complications, improvement of diabetes blood sugar levels, improvement in the physical health and wellbeing of the diabetic and maintenance of an active lifestyle.

The Center provides a unique total care approach for controlling diabetes, involving family members as well. Patients, as well as family members, are taught to do glucose monitoring and when needed to prepare and inject insulin. One patient room has been converted to serve as a permanent classroom for patient and family education, a critical part of care for the diabetic patient.

Proof of the program's impact can be seen by the statistics only two years later in 1992 when the Center served 386 diabetic patients. However, the Center also attracted 37 outpatients in just a few months for various education and counseling assistance.

By 1987 it became clear that the hospital was on a complete upswing from the low points reached in the early 1980s. This was underscored by an article appearing in the March 8, 1987 issue of *Crain's Chicago Business* which compared Norwegian American Hospital's fortunes with those of neighboring Walther Memorial Hospital, which had just declared bankruptcy. Noting that Norwegian American was heading on a course to "post its fourth straight $2 million annual operating surplus," the article commented that the hospital had done all the right things. It had controlled costs when revenues declined, improved relations with its medical staff and provided specialized services demanded in its immediate community."

Specifically, the article noted, "Costs were brought under control by eliminating 55 positions and introducing an innovative, flexible wage system, reducing payroll costs by 8 percent."

In addition, the article said, the hospital helped boost morale among the medical staff by including staff members and officers in planning of future programs. And emphasis was placed on recruiting qualified hispanics, which it noted "comprised 71 percent of Norwegian's medical staff and 81 percent of its patient population."

The article went on to note that the hospital now focuses on three core medical services: obstetrics, pediatrics and family medicine. "Those programs are ideally targeted to capitalize on Humboldt Park's birth rate of 28 per 1,000 – double city and national averages," it commented.

The bottom line, the story continued, was to quote the former administrator, Bill Leyhe, as saying: "We found a market niche in Humboldt Park and were able to tap it profitably by providing competitive and quality services."

With the hospital now in good financial shape, it could continue its efforts to revamp facilities which were old or out of date.

In 1990 it unveiled a brand new $5 million state-of-the-art surgery, opened in response to the pressing need for space and new surgical equipment. Containing a battery of the latest surgical-medical equipment and mechanical features, the new surgery offers the hospital the ability to perform many new procedures and to do them more quickly and with greater safety. It also doubles the amount of space available.

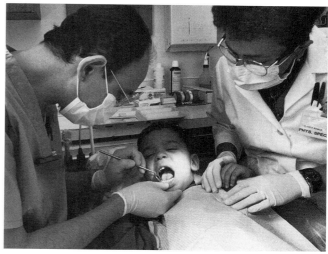

In this 1991 shot taken in the space formerly occupied by the Physician's Specialty Area, young Michael Acevedo, then three years old, cooperates beautifully with Dr. Glasson Souri in having his teeth cleaned. Yolanda Ramos, dental assistant, helps.

According to the former surgery director, Jean Wong, R.N., "Patients can now come in and leave much sooner, or on the same day of the service." Among the suites' new features: laser equipment to facilitate and speed various procedures.

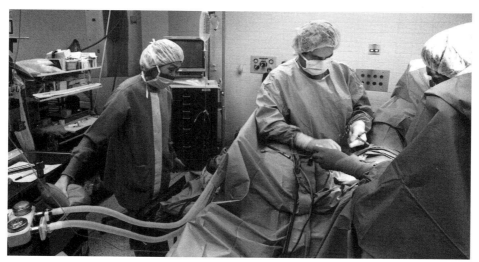

In this shot taken in 1991, surgeon performs a tubal ligation in one of the five new operating rooms. Spacious, bright and state-of-the art, the new surgery greatly enhances the hospital's surgery capabilities.

Under the new setup, the hospital can now perform many new surgical procedures including laparoscopic cholesystectomy (gall bladder removal through the use of a special scope), appendectomy and hysterectomy. It further offers the capability of performing arthroscopy (peering into the knee joint with a special scope) to repair torn tendons and ligaments. Although such surgery is not new to the hospital, many surgeons were reluctant to operate in the old, cramped facilities. This is no longer the case.

Another very useful new feature of the suite is the use of one of the rooms to do Caesarean (C-) Sections when the two rooms in the LDR suite, where such procedures are ordinarily performed, are overflowing.

In addition, one room can be used for outpatient (one-day) surgery and for urology, but not exclusively, according to Ms. Wong.

A very helpful feature is offered by one of the rooms which is lead lined and offers the use of a special C-Arm X-ray unit, which gives off radiation. Through use of the C-Arm, surgeons are now able to view inside a patient's body as they work. The C-Arm is very useful in such procedures as hip-pinning, as it guides the surgeon to see exactly where the pinning is to be performed by observing the procedure on the C-Arm monitor.

In addition, the new suite is completely sprinklered and features a dry system which gives off air when a sensor goes off. And it now offers space to store stretchers in a nearby closet, thus avoiding the possibilities of staff tripping over them, as was formerly the case.

To access the unit, doctors and support staff – nurses and housekeeping personnel – enter through the lounge area, directly below, on the fourth floor. The locker room area is equipped with toilet facilities and sleeping rooms for on-call personnel. All surgery personnel entering the operating room suite first change into surgical scrubs on the fourth floor and then ascend the stairs leading to the operating room suite. Personnel that have no business in the area are unable to enter since only those with the proper access codes can enter.

With the new surgery in operation, the hospital could now offer greater service to both patients and medical staff and could perform a variety of new procedures which in turn will generate new business and income for the hospital.

Closely related to the new surgery suite was the outpatient surgery department, or Surgicenter, a new unit where patients are scheduled for one-day surgery on an outpatient basis.

Under the Same Day Surgery (as it is called) setup, patients come to the unit a day or two prior to their scheduled surgery and go through a battery of preadmission testing, including blood testing, checking their electrocardiogram, and so forth.

They then return to the Surgicenter, a day or two later for surgery, where they are assigned a bed and given a pre-operative physical, and then visited by an anesthesiologist the morning of the surgery. The patient is then transferred to the new surgery on the fifth floor where the procedure is performed, after which they are taken to the recovery room and

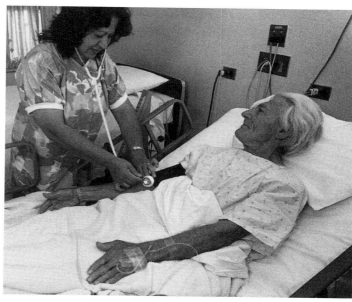

One of the most rapidly growing departments in the hospital is Unit 3B – Same Day Surgery, otherwise known as the surgicenter. In this shot taken in 1991 Nurse Assistant Maria Rodriguez ministers to the needs of elderly patient in the hospital for cataract surgery.

closely observed – until their vital signs: blood pressure, pulse and breathing – are stabilized while the anesthesia wears off.

If there are no complications by the end of the day (about 6 p.m. or so) the patient is discharged. If however there are complications, patients are kept overnight for further observation.

In 1991 the hospital felt secure enough in its resources, both in manpower and finances, to terminate its contract with Brim & Associates for executive counsel and supervision, to appoint its own top executive officers. Clarence Nagelvoort was appointed vice president of the hospital in May of 1991 and in August of that same year he was appointed Executive Vice President.

Others promoted to top executive ranks were Mary Toma, Vice President of Patient Care Services, who assumed the position of Executive Vice President and Chief Operating Officer, and Thomas McFarland, Vice President and Chief Financial Officer.

Two new programs which saw their initiation in 1991 were first the formation of the Century Physician Hospital Organization, a partnership of the medical staff physicians and the hospital to contract for medical services to managed care organizations, such as Health Maintenance Organizations (HMO's) and Physician Provider Organizations (PPO's).

The other organization, Centennial Medical Management Corporation, is a for profit subsidiary of the hospital holding company – Norwegian American Health Systems. As such, it handles professional services rendered by either the doctors or the hospital, which are not included in the contract with Century PHO. CMMC contracts for physicians and provides physician billing and benefit support and operates in much the same manner as a group medical practice.

While everything that we have described in this chapter has a positive spin, not everything that happens even in the best run hospitals is for the best and Norwegian American has had its failures as well – for example, the financial crunches of the late '20s and the early 1980s and what could have been a crippling strike in the early '70s. But there have been other setbacks as well. A good example is a liability suit against the hospital and two of its top ranked physicians in connection with the delivery of a newborn infant after the infant suffered irreversible damages arising from the administration of too much oxygen during the delivery. The hospital and the physicians were sued for $11 million in damages in 1983. The case dragged on for several years, and eventually a settlement was reached with the plaintiff, for $5 million. It was the kind of an incident which can happen any time at any hospital and one for which hospitals must ever be watchful to prevent any recurrences. Because of the rising frequency of such liability suits, many of them frivolous, hospitals have had to protect themselves with expensive malpractice insurance, which adds considerably to the cost of operations.

Beyond this, the hospital continued to explore affiliations with other healthcare providers to assure a continuity of care for its patients to allow it to participate more fully with larger managed care organizations.

Apparently the hospital was on the right track. Attention to basic operating strategies and the hospital mission paid off as the hospital was rewarded in 1992 with the finest net income from operations ever recorded in its 96 continuous years of operation: $6.1 million, of which $4.8 million was reinvested in the hospital and $1.3 million added to the depreciation account.

All signs indicated a strong recovery from the dark days of the early '80s with the hospital showing a resurgence in admissions, deliveries, surgical cases and emergency visits.

The year also saw renewed emphasis on campus enhancement. Attention once again focused on the completion of many improvements in security, parking, landscaping and facilities. As part of the overall improvement plan, the hospital acquired new real estate in the area to allow for future expansion. In return it donated land to the neighboring Trinity Lutheran Church and assisted in the construction of a new building for the church with $100,000 in matching funds.

In keeping with its commitment to child and health safety, Norwegian American sponsored its third annual bilingual Kid Safe Conference at Roberto Clemente High School. The award-winning program is aimed at providing parents and children with hands-on training in emergency first-aid, fire safety, personal safety, responsible babysitting, CPR, drug abuse prevention, and other aspects of personal safety and security.

More than 250 participated in the day-long event which featured many activities. After a brief opening ceremony featuring Sheila Lyne, then Health Commissioner of the City of Chicago, and other city and state officials, the children and their parents attended various safety workshops

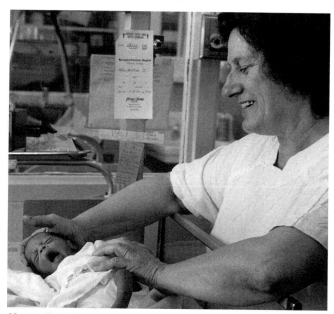

Norma Rog, RN, a 1942 graduate of the NAH School of Nursing, is seen with one of her little ones. Ms. Rog, whose work was obviously pleasurable, retired after 21 years of service in the Nursery.

presented by representatives of local, community, city and statewide agencies, all aimed at familiarizing the children with what to do when confronted with emergencies threatening their safety or security.

As the hospital approached its Centennial Year, 1993-94, a Centennial Committee was established to plan and oversee all of the Hospital's special events for this milestone year. To begin the process, the Committee, headed by Board Chairman Norman R. Dahl, gathered during a special retreat in February, 1993. To celebrate this gala event, the Committee had planned 100 Centennial events, to include all areas of the hospital community – volunteers, administration, patients, and community residents. The Centennial years, 1993-94 were to be banner years, the likes of which Norwegian American Hospital had not seen in its century-long history.

CHAPTER 8

The Hospital Centennial: A Time of Celebration and Triumph

The hospital's Centennial year, 1993-94, was special in many respects celebrating as it did 100 years of dedicated service to the Humboldt Park community and surrounding neighborhoods on Chicago's Northwest side. The year started off with a truly unique mission of mercy to medically deprived and underserved countries in Latin America and the Philippines. It was a completely new and unique venture for the hospital aimed at providing medical care and treatment to the needy and ill in distant foreign lands.

In launching the missions, the hospital was breaking new ground in its operations. The idea was that while the Humboldt Park residents remain the top priority and objective in meeting the healthcare needs of the community, the needs of those in other lands cannot and should not be ignored. Basically, people in developing countries often have no access to even simple medical care. Often local physicians are completely isolated from training or information about new technology and the latest in medical techniques. Even those able to reach medical facilities and providers often cannot afford such care. Given such conditions, even the smallest illness can be life threatening. And if a relatively simple and routine procedure such as a cataract removal is unavailable or too costly, it can lead to a lifetime of blindness.

In response to the overwhelming needs of such medically deprived peoples in various lands in Asia and Latin America, in 1992-93 the hospital, its medical staff and the Board committed itself to lending a helping hand to several foreign countries: Colombia, Bolivia, the Philippines, followed by Missions to Mexico and Peru in the Spring of 1994.

The first Mission, to Cartagena, Colombia, coincided with the celebration of the 175th anniversary of Cartagena University. Several physicians in the Norwegian American contingent are graduates of this renowned university in the Western Hemisphere and were anxious to share their knowledge with local residents. Led by the then Board Chairman Norman R. Dahl, a medical team headed by Drs. Everildes and Luis Yarzagaray, lectured about contagious diseases, heart problems, hematology, cancer and other medical subjects. In addition they contributed valves used in neurosurgery, valued at $10,000, and $15,000, and other medical supplies including catheters, fluids, gloves and syringes to university medical teams.

A second mission, to Sucre, Bolivia was spearheaded by Dr. Enrique A. Arana, Dr. Eduardo Barriuso and Dr. Rafael Campanini, with the support of the newly formed Century Lions Club of Norwegian American Hospital. Prominent in the contingent of doctors taking part in the mission were two ophthalmologists, Dr. Osvaldo Lopez and Dr. Robert Weiss, who were joined by local medical personnel in examining hundreds in a clinic for poverty-stricken residents of the area, who were treated for various eye problems, including cataracts.

A third mission was set up to care for the needs of poor and needy people in Manila. Numbering more than 30 hospital physicians, nurses and administrative personnel (all members of the Century Lions Club) the clinic personnel examined patients for a variety of conditions ranging from cataract, harelip, and other birth defects as well as women suffering from complications of pregnancy and others requiring plastic surgery. An estimated one thousand patients were seen and treated during the week-long clinic.

As part of the Mission to the Philippines, hospital Board Chairman Norman R. Dahl, who accompanied the mission, noted that the group was offering clinic participants participation in the Lions SightFirst program aimed at eliminating blindness throughout the world by the year 2000.

While in Manila, participating mission doctors saw a cross section of Manila's poor and sick. Mission doctors represented various medical specialties and were well equipped to treat nearly all conditions uncovered in the course of the mission, said Dahl.

Cooperating in the mission were representatives of local Lions Clubs in Manila who provided transportation for patients to and from the clinic and in scheduling patients.

Commenting on the Mission, Dahl noted that the concept had originated when, as a member of the Lions International Board, he stopped off in Manila upon his return from a meeting in India in 1992 to see the city's Mayor. Noting the many physicians on the staff at Norwegian American Hospital of Filipino background, the Mayor indicated his desire to arrange a medical mission to the Philippines.

The matter was put to the hospital's medical staff and approved as part of the Centennial celebration, and the hospital's Board approved the funding that would be required to make the mission a reality.

Besides providing supplies and equipment as well as medical personnel, the hospital provided transportation to the Philippines and lodging for mission participants while in Manila.

Dr. Henry Munez, chairman of the hospital's Pediatrics department, served as Mission Chairman and was accompanied by several surgeons, a urologist, a plastic surgeon, an ophthal-

Clarence Nagelvoort, former hospital President and Chief Executive Officer, was in the midst of things as this shot taken during the Medical Mission to the Philippines in 1998 clearly shows.

mologist, several obstetrician-gynecologists and other family practice doctors.

As noted above, additional medical missions to Mexico and Peru were scheduled for Spring of 1994. Since the inception of the hospital's historic medical outreach program, Norwegian American Hospital has sponsored a total of 16 medical missions to foreign lands.

As a fortunate, but unforeseen result of the missions to the Philippines and to Bolivia, several young children suffering from various crippling and disfiguring birth defects were flown to Norwegian American Hospital where they were successfully treated and flown back to their homelands. There they are expected to be able to lead normal lives. They included a Filipino toddler, Maria Ugardo, then 18 months, suffering from a grapefruit size growth on her forehead known as a meningocele, who will be able to lead a normal life thanks to surgery she had received later at Norwegian American Hospital.

The second child was a Bolivian boy, Marcelo Fernandez, nine years old when he came to the attention of Lions participating in the mission to Sucre, Bolivia. Marcelo was born with congenital cataracts which threatened him with a lifetime of blindness. The third child was little Lawrence Baile, born prematurely with his bladder outside of his body and without a sex organ. He was only a few months old when his mother brought him to the second hospital-sponsored mission to Manila in 1994.

In the case of nine-year-old Marcelo Fernandez, who was rejected by his family because of his threatened blindness, the boy walked an estimated 60 kilometers so that he could be seen by physicians participating in the first mission in Sucre in 1993. There he was seen by Dr. Osvaldo Lopez, one of the participating ophthalmologists, who that same night removed the cataract from one of the boy's eyes.

Later young Marcelo, accompanied by a Bolivian physician, arrived in Chicago on Easter Sunday 1994. A few days later, Dr. Lopez performed the surgery to remove the remaining cataract and the boy has received lens implants. Now with treatment and follow-up, young Marcelo is assured of being able to see and to lead a normal life.

In the case of little Maria Ugardo, the child with the growth on her forehead, she arrived at the hospital only a few hours before Marcelo on Easter Sunday. With the massive growth on her forehead delaying little Maria's normal development, her parents had been assured that surgery would be required to remove the growth.

Only a few days after her arrival, the growth was removed by a hospital neurosurgeon, Dr. Luis Yarzagaray, who was quietly optimistic about the child's further development after the surgery. He was assisted in the surgery by Dr. Renato Imana, head of neurosurgery at Central DuPage Hospital. To make things even more joyful, the child's mother, who was well along in her pregnancy when arriving at the hospital, gave birth to a healthy baby boy at Norwegian American. She named the baby Norman Henry, in honor of Board Chairman Norman R. Dahl and Dr. Henry Munez, head of pediatrics at NAH, who had served as medical mission chairman.

Because of the wide exposure the case received in the nation's news media: It was on CNN, where it was seen by millions, and an estimated 9 TV cameras were

Marcelo Fernandez, the nine year old Bolivian boy born with congenital cataracts of both eyes which threatened him with a lifetime of blindness. Thanks to the surgery he received at Norwegian American in 1994, Marcelo is assured of being able to resume his life in a rural area of Bolivia. In the first shot he is accompanied by a physician from his native country upon arrival at the hospital. In the second shot, Marcelo admires his bicycle, one of many gifts he received following completion of the surgery on his eyes.

on hand the day of the surgery to feed news of the outcome to additional millions. With such exposure, viewers sent in thousands of dollars to help meet expenses which might accrue in days to come. These were put into a special fund administered by former Manila Mayor Ramon Bagatsing and Counselor Felix Espiritu. Of the $5,000 originally placed in the fund, an estimated $4,000 still remains to help meet future expenses which may be incurred in the youngster's recovery.

In the last and the most recent case, that of little Lawrence Baile, the child's parents had been advised that it would cost thousands of dollars to obtain the corrective surgery that it

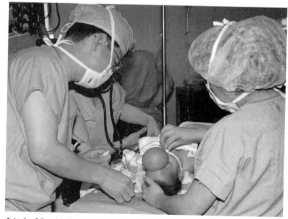

Little Maria Ugardo, 18 month old Filipino toddler born with a grapefruit size growth on her forehead, undergoes surgery at Norwegian American Hospital several days after her arrival in 1994. As a result of the surgery, she is expected to be able to lead a fairly normal life in her native country.

would take to enable Lawrence to urinate normally. But when he was only seven months old, the child's chances for a normal life brightened when his mother, carrying the baby in her arms, showed the attending physician her child. Deeply touched, the doctor told her that the hospital and the Lions Club would help. True to their words, when Lawrence was four and strong enough for the surgery, he and his mother were flown to Chicago for the required surgery at Norwegian American Hospital.

Earlier as a result of surgery performed in 1994 during the hospital's second mission to the Philippines, the child had undergone the first stage of his treatment, involving the closure of the bladder and the abdominal wall. To take care of this part of the treatment, Lawrence's pelvis had to be opened to move the organs inside his body to create an opening at the abdomen to enable him to urinate.

The next phase of the surgery, which was performed at Norwegian American, saw Dr. Guillermo Gonzales, a urologist at NAH, and Dr. Casimir Firlit, chairman of pediatric urology at Chicago's Children's Memorial Hospital, handling phase two of the surgery, involving bladder neck reconstruction, penile elongation and reconstruction and urethoplasty, or the closure of the open urethra.

In all three cases, hospital expenses of from $70,000 to $80,000 per child, were paid for by the hospital's philanthropic arm, the Norwegian American Hospital Foundation, while the surgeons' services were provided free of charge. Board and lodging for Maria's and Lawrence's mothers, were donated by Norwegian American Hospital's Century Lions Club. With the help of the hospital and the humanitarian physicians and staff participating in the surgery, and the hospital's Century Lions Club, all three youngsters have been assured of being able to enjoy fairly normal lives, thus closing out one of the most dramatic and humanitarian chapters in the history of Norwegian American Hospital.

In the words of Dr. Eduardo Ladlad, then president of the medical staff, "I was proud to be a part of the medical team headed by Dr. Henry Munez, that represented NAH to the people of the Philippines. Our return, at the time of the Thanksgiving holiday, gives us all pause to reflect on the significance of our work in the historical tradition of Norwegian American Hospital. Making contributions like these to the world community has its own rewards."

But the treatment of the three children described in the paragraphs above and the thousands of other poor and needy seen during the Medical Missions to Latin America and the Philippines was only one phase of the hospital's Centennial celebration.

The year-long celebration got underway officially with the kickoff dinner in October, 1993 held at the Field Museum. There 800 guests were wined and dined and superbly entertained by Carol Lawrence in the vast expanse of the museum.

The Christmas holidays brought renewed opportunities for taking part in the annual Giving Tree project. This annual

On hand to participate in the Centennial Festivities celebrating 100 years of service by the hospital to the Humboldt Park and surrounding areas was Mayor Richard Daley (at left). In center is Arabel Rosales, then Assistant to Governor Jim Edgar, while Norman R. Dahl, then hospital Chairman of the Board, is at the right.

event, which provides needy families with gifts and food, was bigger than ever as 100 families were enabled to celebrate the holidays with newfound joy thanks to the Woman's Board, which coordinated the event.

The 1994's start saw the launching of many special activities intended to focus on the Centennial celebration and on Norwegian American Hospital's role as good neighbor and key healthcare provider. Many health screenings and brochures were provided for community residents and staff members. A good example was the open house held in Cardiology, which included free blood pressure screenings and health literature. Another event, in the area of parenting, taught participants how to handle a variety of troublesome home situations in a positive way.

Spring saw the arrival of many special visitors to Norwegian American, including Norway's prime minister, Mrs. Gro Harlem Brundtland and her husband, in May. Mrs. Brundtland, who was in town for a speaking engagement, found time to visit Norwegian American. A physician, she is especially interested in healthcare issues and hospital technology, and healthcare practices in community hospitals. That same evening a reception and dinner were held in her honor. Guests included the Norwegian Ambassador to the United States and the retiring and incoming U.S. Ambassadors to Norway.

Mrs. Brundtland, in her remarks, praised the hospital for "seeing such a wonderful legacy of the Norwegian community here, now serving the Hispanic community."

And King Harald V of Norway, accompanied by Queen Sonja, took part in ground-breaking ceremonies for the new Professional Building.

On hand to participate at the groundbreaking of the Professional Medical Building and tree planting in connection with the hospital's Centennial was King Harald V of Norway (center). Standing by are Clarence Nagelvoort, former President and Chief Executive Officer (left) and Norman R. Dahl, former Hospital Board Chairman.

Yet another famous visitor to the hospital was four-time Olympic gold medalist skater, Norway's Johann Olav Koss, who stopped off for a visit on a tour of the United States.

As a Norwegian and a medical student, he gave priority to visiting Norwegian American and in response the hospital hosted a luncheon in his honor, and presented him with a gold watch.

At the luncheon Norman R. Dahl, board chairman and trustee, told the audience: "As a four-time gold medalist in Lillehammer and a medical student, he is an outstanding example for young people around the globe."

Came the 4th of July and the hospital hosted yet another special Centennial event: the dedication of the Centennial Promenade. Located across from the hospital, the promenade was part of the hospital's extensive beautification plan then nearing completion. Featured are flags of Chicago, the United States, Norway, Lions Club International and a special hospital flag. Attending were many community residents who, with other area residents, now enjoy this attractive area the year-round.

Shortly afterward, the promenade was the site of the Norwegian American Hospital Centennial Health Mission presented for area residents. A variety of health screenings for those 14 and over was provided for community residents, together with entertainment, refreshments, gifts and health literature.

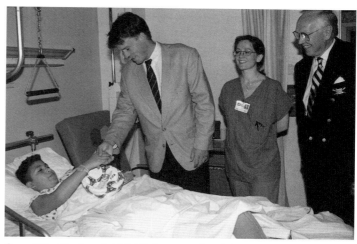

For the balance of the summer, the promenade area and a special tent served as the site of many additional community events. The International Festival, for example, featured a variety of talented entertainers. Also featured were carnival rides for the children and a variety of ethnic foods to sample.

Another event which proved quite popular was the Teddy Bear Health Fair, also held in the Centennial tent. During the one-day free health fair, many health services were provided children ages, 3-12. The youngsters had the

One of the Centennial highlights was the visit to the hospital of Johann Olav Koss, four-time Olympic Gold medal skating champion, shown with young patient in the orthopedics area. Per Bye Ohrstrom, Norwegian Consul General in Chicago, is at the right.

opportunity to tour an ambulance and to meet medical personnel in a non-threatening environment.

These were but a few of the more than 100 special events undertaken to keep the Centennial in the public eye all year. Indeed there was something for everyone. Making the events possible and as successful as they turned out to be were the thousands of manhours of planning and coordination donated by volunteers. In addition many hospital staff members, administrators and friends handled numerous additional tasks to make the year's events possible.

Adding a festive touch to the celebration were a series of banners decorating light posts on each of the main streets surrounding the hospital campus. The banners, one in Spanish and the other in English, proclaimed to passersby: "Your Family Hospital Since 1894." Also very much a part of the festival were a series of commercials aired on Channel 44 bringing the hospital to the public's attention in connection with the Centennial. Featured in each segment of the series was a physician who gave advice and counsel on various health problems. This and many other colorful events, such as a wine and cheese reception for artists of the community, helped to focus attention on Norwegian American Hospital and what it has meant to the community as a primary provider of health care and community booster for more than a century.

Perhaps one of the most significant of the various events held to celebrate the Centennial was the formation of the hospital's own Lions Club – the Norwegian American Hospital Century Lions Club. Headed by Dr. Eduardo Ladlad, then president of both the medical staff and the Lions Club, the newly-formed club aimed at recruiting 100 members of the hospital and medical staff. One of its first and most dramatic activities was to help underwrite, man and support the various Medical Missions to Latin America and the Philippines described above.

But the Centennial Year celebration was just a prelude of the events and achievements yet to come. These are described in the chapter that follows.

CHAPTER 9

A Year of Expansion and New Hope for the Future

If 1993-94 was a year of celebration and reaffirmation of the role Norwegian American Hospital has played in caring for the sick and the infirm in the Humboldt Park and surrounding areas, it was also a year of new hope and expansion.

The programs undertaken in the years preceding the Centennial – the renovation of the delivery rooms, the expansion of the nursery and the pediatrics department and ultimately the initiation and construction of the technologically superb surgery suite – had to be continued to meet the healthcare needs of community residents. So, building on those accomplishments, an entire array of improvements was launched during 1993.

Perhaps the most substantial, and certainly one of the most needed of these improvements, was the complete renovation and expansion of the Emergency Room. In the works for several years, the new Emergency Room opened its doors in its new quarters in April 1993. By almost doubling its size, the new facility could increase the number of treatment bays from three to ten, including several cribs for infants, two surgical beds for minor surgery, such as suturing and small incisions, and a cast room to handle among others, fractures of the arms and legs.

Patients coming into the new Emergency Room are now seen more quickly and are assured of receiving improved treatment. Under the new setup patients can be kept in designated areas or until the case is taken care of and the patient is ready for discharge.

Staff of Pilsen Clinic on West 18th Street, one of 10 ProHealth Community Health Clinics operated by the Hospital six days a week. Hours vary, depending on the clinic.

Further, if a small child comes in with a high fever, a common emergency room problem, personnel can place the youngster in the emergency holding area instead of in the department waiting room, together with other sick patients, both young and old.

If a patient comes in with abdominal pain or vaginal bleeding for instance, and the pain is intolerable, the staff can stabilize the patient in the Emergency Room and take a blood test to see if infection is present or not. Following this initial treatment, the patient can wait in relative comfort until the test results needed to confirm the diagnosis are obtained.

The department now includes four beds in the critical care area with monitors and equipment to handle cardiac arrest (heart attacks). Other equipment of proven merit include three electronic blood pressure monitors, two cribs, adult and infant scales, and three new portable trays for IV's (intravenous blood, medications or nutrition), phlebotomy and wound or burn dressings. A library with the most current reference material is also on hand for physicians and nurses.

A much desired aspect of the new facility is the increase in professional staffing, enabling personnel in this very busy area to more quickly assess and treat patients. In the year preceding, nearly 25,000 patients were seen, an achievement made possible by the enlarged and better equipped area. Patients are now treated even more promptly by competent staff working 365 days a week, 24 hours a day.

Then in 1996 the Emergency Room was upgraded from Standby to Comprehensive status. Now the department can accept patients brought in by fire department or private ambulances. As a result, an additional 4,000 seriously injured or very sick patients are treated in the Emergency Room every year.

1993 also saw several major improvements in the five clinical centers (now ten) in the hospital's service area, which were combined under the ProHealth banner. Located throughout the hospital service area, the clinics bring together a uniquely qualified team of pediatricians, gynecologists, internists, surgeons, podiatrists, family practitioners and obstetricians. As a result, the clinics are able to handle the vast majority of the health problems and injuries that present themselves. But in addition, ProHealth physicians treat not only patients who are sick, but they also counsel patients on proven techniques in nutrition, diet and living, to help them stay well and to prevent disease and various other health problems.

During 1992-93, the five ProHealth Centers then scattered throughout the hospital community served nearly 14,000 patients of all ages. All offered convenient hours, including Saturdays. While each center is aimed at providing primary care or performing routine child and infant examinations, treating upper respiratory infections, and backaches, patients requiring further testing or treatment are referred to the main hospital.

By 1998 the number of clinics under the ProHealth Banner had increased to 10 and they were averaging a total of 3,200 patients per month. The number is increasing steadily, according to Janina Nieves, RN, former Director of Ambulatory Services.

Besides offering convenient office hours, each clinic further provides complete health screenings once a week for such conditions as diabetes, high blood pressure and arthritis. Through such screenings, many conditions are caught in the early stages which otherwise could become major health problems.

In addition, hospital educators visit clinics on an alternating basis each month to discuss diabetes with local residents, both in English and in Spanish. One clinic, on Western Avenue, offers a service known as Total Health Care for Seniors. For a slight fee, the service offers transportation to and from the clinic, discounts on prescriptions filled at the hospital, as well as free screenings for diabetes and high blood pressure, and priority registration if hospital services are required.

All of the clinics are networked by computerized record-keeping and billing for greater speed and efficiency. In addition, they are advertised and promoted widely in newspapers, and on the radio in both Spanish and English; clinic physicians are all completely bilingual.

Another greatly anticipated improvement in patient services was the move in 1993 of the GI Lab to new and expanded quarters on the third floor; it had previously been a part of the Emergency Room. The new facility greatly increases the Lab's ability to handle gastrointestinal procedures and to increase manpower efficiency.

According to Illuminada Gold, R.N., Clinical Nurse Manager of the G.I. Lab, the department is used primarily for screening purposes. For example, colonoscopy involves the use of a special scope to help detect colon cancer, a disease which is becoming increasingly common. Another scope is used commonly to perform gastroscopy, to help detect peptic ulcers, stomach polyps, or bleeding in the stomach.

Another improvement in the hospital's ability to treat patients who are quite ill was the expansion of the telemetry unit from 8 to 22 beds. In telemetry, patients' heart rates, blood pressures and other vital signs are closely monitored while they are recuperating from surgery or serious illness.

According to Rosalina Robles, R.N., Coordinator of ICU-Telemetry, patients assigned to the ICU (Intensive Care Unit) are monitored very closely with a catheter that is inserted through their arteries into the heart; there is one nurse for every two patients and the average length of stay is one day.

In telemetry, patients are also monitored but not as closely as in ICU. They are connected to a portable box which monitors their heart rate, pulse and other vital signs. Here patients, not as critically ill as those in Intensive Care, are observed from one central observation station. They may be ambulatory or confined to bed. There is one nurse for every five patients in telemetry.

But of all the improvements initiated at the hospital in recent years, certainly the most impressive and in many ways the most dramatic, is the new five-story

Impressive new Professional Building dedicated in 1997 at a cost of $11 million. The new facility, which adds 60,000 square feet to the hospital, was completely paid for before it was built.

Professional Building. Constructed and opened in 1997 at a cost of $11 million, the handsome new building projects, an exceptional positive image on the original hospital by providing state-of-the-art outpatient and office facilities, a new and spacious hospital lobby, and a comfortable waiting area.

The 60,000 square feet structure has a common entranceway on both Cortez and Thomas Streets, thus doubling the size of the lobby and enhancing the appearance of the entire hospital complex. Besides offering office space for physicians (completely leased by the time the building opened in 1997), the new facility offers expanded space for what has been termed the Outpatient Department, but which is more properly known as the Physician's Specialty Center as well as the Family Health Center.

Janina Nieves, R.N. and former Director of Ambulatory Services, at the reception desk of the new Family Health Center. Spacious, bright and cheerful, the new department has helped to relieve some of the congestion of the old quarters, which saw patients spilling into the corridors.

Convenient and accessible to both physicians and patients, the area is one of the busiest of the hospital, so much so that it was literally bursting at the seams, with patients spilling out into the corridor while waiting to see a doctor, prior to the construction of the new building.

In its new quarters, the Physician's Specialty Center is set up to handle a much greater number of patients, and with more comfort. It now also includes the Family Health Center, where patients can see physicians for healthcare services not offered in the Physician's Specialty Area.

According to Janina Nieves, R.N., former Director of Ambulatory (outpatient) Services, patients referred to the Physician's Specialty Center can receive laser treatment for cataract and for many other eye conditions from several ophthalmologists four days a week. Other patients visit the center twice a week for foot problems, where they are seen by several podiatrists; still others with problems of the back, hips, knees and other parts of the musculoskeletal system, see orthopedic physicians twice a week, and finally there are specialists in ear, nose and throat, otherwise known as ENT, who are available at the center twice a week to see patients.

The Family Health Service, on the other hand, is staffed by physicians specializing in obstetrics-gynecology who can provide services to pregnant women or to women referred from the West Town Clinic.

Also on hand at the Center are dermatologists, specializing in skin problems and problems relating to hair loss, and pediatric cardiologists, who see children referred to the Center who have heart problems.

Finally, the Center offers several neurologists, who see patients referred with nerve disorders, epilepsy, brain damage or brain tumors.

In the near future the Physician's Specialty Center is scheduled to handle minor eye surgery such as Chalazions (better known as sties) and other eye growths. Such surgery, utilizing local anesthesia, will be performed at lower patient cost, since it involves same day surgery. The patient comes in one day and after the surgery is completed, leaves later that same day. All preadmission work – lab and x-ray for example – is done prior to the surgery, thus avoiding keeping the patient in the hospital overnight at higher cost.

Aside from the space currently being leased for physicians' offices, the other major occupant of the new Professional Office Building is the Women's Health Center, opened December 4, 1997 and begun with funds supplied by the Norwegian American Hospital Foundation, the Hospital's charitable arm. It takes a holistic approach to women's health and is concerned with answering a wide array of women's needs and services in a comfortable, home-like setting. Programs currently offered include patient education, teen pregnancy prevention, classes for expectant mothers and fathers, breast cancer screenings and gynecological oncology (cancer treatment and diagnosis). Plans for the future call for the establishment of a resource center for community residents and massage therapy.

Leonor Munez, former President of the Women's Board, and President of the Norwegian American Hospital Foundation.

While a major focus of the Women's Health Center is devoted to delivery of babies, the emphasis is on major women's concerns, such as menopause and family planning.

All in all, the new Professional Office Building has covered some major gaps in Norwegian American Hospital's ability to meet patient and physician needs and is thriving in the short time it has been open.

That brings our story of Norwegian American Hospital up to date – its early struggles, triumphs and its ability to change with changing community needs, and all of this in the face of rising costs, lower patient population and shorter hospital stays.

What the future holds for the hospital is still open to question, but the hospital management and its Board of Trustees is working on plans to take Norwegian American Hospital into the 21st century and to make the transition as smooth and meaningful as ever. As this is being written, plans are being made to make the hospital even more serviceable and responsive to community needs. These will be discussed in Chapter 11.

CHAPTER 10

A Look at the Future

As Norwegian American Hospital swings into the 21st Century, it has a lot going for it. This includes a loyal and dedicated management staff – possibly the most professional ever – with the credentials to face the challenges posed by new technology and techniques of patient care. There is also a new emphasis on patient wellness and disease prevention. It also has possibly the largest and most responsive medical staff in its history – one capable of handling at least 90 percent of the cases that present themselves to physicians – either at their offices or at the ProHealth Satellite Clinics, Emergency Room, or at the Family Health Center or Physician's Specialty Center.

In addition the hospital is in good shape financially. The new Professional Office Building was paid for before it was built. To quote the then Chairman of the Board, Norman R. Dahl: "The mortgage debt that we had when I first joined the Board in 1965 is gone and we still have reserves that can provide the funds to carry us if there should be a shortfall."

As to the hospital's strengths, Dahl notes that "in the area of newborns – we have had as many as 4,300 in one year recently and while it has probably dropped to about 3,000 a year in recent years, the number of deliveries will probably rise again because mothers who have had their babies here will want to return because they know that this is our strength."

Dahl notes that the hospital has assembled an outstanding medical staff and has expanded the role of the oncology clinic (especially with regard to the newly initiated Women's Health Center). He is optimistic about the ten clinics acquired in outlying areas – the ProHealth satellite clinics – which have brought additional thousands of patients into the hospital. They come either as in-patients suffering from acute illness or outpatients utilizing the new Family Health and Physician's Specialty Centers.

"In the past five years we have poured about $20 million into the hospital, plus about $11 million for the professional building – in other words in excess of $30 million. And this has all been made possible through expert management," he observed.

As to future usages of the main hospital building, Dahl says, "As the need arises, we may use the old hospital building as an extended care or nursing home facility for those suffering from such illnesses as cancer or heart disease, who have need for such facilities."

But for the immediate future, he says, the hospital must focus on "raising a sizeable amount of funds. It must focus on outpatient care, one-day surgery, expanded emergency visits, and so forth."

For acutely ill patients, he foresees the need for a hospital building of about 150 beds or less. To meet the cost for constructing the new facility, he estimates the hospital will require $80 million, not including the land.

When will this take effect? Possibly in the next five to ten years, says Dahl, noting, "We are going to have to put an estimated $20 million into renovating the hospital to bring it up to code," and he poses the question of whether it might not be more practical to start the building of the new facility by constructing the first floors, two above ground and one below, and completing the rest of the facility as need requires.

"It would be located just north of the current hospital building and would be bound by Division Street to the north, Thomas to the south.

"This is something that we must be ready to implement, although it's hard to say just when we will proceed. This may not happen during my lifetime, but at least the planning will be there, the land will be cleared and we will be able to go ahead."

He notes that the hospital has acquired all the land required for the new building, except for a few parcels out of about 40.

Dahl points to the recently signed affiliation agreement with Illinois Masonic Hospital as a step in the right direction.

While many hospitals have set up networks of affiliations with other major healthcare providers, this usually has involved the expenditure of major sums of money. "Typically hospitals spend $5 million to $10 million to form such affiliations," he commented.

"We did ours for virtually nothing but the attorney's fees," he adds. It was a very minimal amount.

Under the agreement, Illinois Masonic is Norwegian American Hospital's partner for provision of tertiary services. These are services that Norwegian American is not currently set up to handle. For example, Level III (very critically ill babies) would be sent to Illinois Masonic. It would also supply MRI imaging services, which Norwegian American currently cannot offer, and other such services as advanced oncology (cancer) treatment, cardiac catheterization, still the most reliable test for imaging the heart and arteries leading to the heart, open heart (bypass) surgery and a range of services not presently provided by Norwegian American.

Dahl further noted that Illinois Masonic would "assist us in our Emergency Room by providing services that we cannot currently offer, such as neurosurgery and a staff of infectious disease specialists for diagnosis and treatment of such diseases."

In return, he observes, "Illinois Masonic would receive referrals (those very sick or tertiary care patients) that we cannot currently handle. They would also help us to expand primary care services in supporting us in raising the level of service that we provide, for instance allowing us to do more in the areas of oncology or emergency medicine."

A point of pride, he notes with some satisfaction, is the medical staff. "We have some 300 doctors on staff, all of whom interact with the management and have been very supportive of management in helping to make needed improvements.

"And we have seen more specialists coming aboard our staff in the last three years – some of the top people in the Midwest. Many have joined our staff through their exposure received through the medical missions to Latin America and to the Philippines. The latter have been very helpful in recruiting physicians and highlight the fact that here at Norwegian American we provide medical missions every day of the year."

Members of the medical staff are caught in conference in the Doctors' Conference Room. Left to right are: Pedro Lopez, M.D., then Director; Patricia Jones, Director of Medical Affairs; Howard Lopata, M.D., then Director of the Medical Staff and Director of Radiology; Enrique Arana, M.D., Chairman, Family Practice; and Rafael Campanini, M.D., Chairman of Pathology.

"The major challenge to the future, as I see it," he notes, "is to be aware of what is happening around you – being able to predict in order to control the destiny of the hospital. Some risks must be taken," he continues. "Clearly, in the future, hospital leadership must be focused on patient care quality as well as financial responsibility," he adds.

"In recent years we have had the tremendous benefit of technology," he observed, "enabling us to offer services and care that were inconceivable only a few years ago. This in turn has lessened the needs in many ways for hospital services by enabling people to live longer."

But, he commented, "We have an aging population. We will have more senior citizens in the next 30 years than ever before in the United States, and these people will need care so there will be less extra capacity in the hospital than there is now."

Certainly a big factor which will affect the hospital's financial standing and its ability to recruit physicians is managed care, otherwise known as health maintenance organizations and physician provider services. Set up in the early 1960s as a means of offering more complete healthcare coverage, both medical and hospitalization, HMO's are the preferred means of coverage for most Americans today. They usually offer preventive medicine, aimed at keeping the consumer well and avoiding medical problems, as well as the more conventional coverage. While the coverage is often much more comprehensive than that offered by most traditional plans, the drawback is that the patient is limited in choice of physician, and is restricted to physicians who are members of the HMO. While they are more comprehensive than standard health insurance plans, they often contain exclusions for such care as vision and hearing problems and there often are caps (limits to how much can be spent on any given case).

Further complicating the picture is the impact of utilization review boards. Since their introduction in the mid-'60s, the federal government, HMO's and private insurance programs are all making increasingly extensive use of such boards. To admit a patient to the hospital, a physician must be able to document the need for such hospitalization to the Utilization Review Board. Not only does the board pass on which patients can be admitted, but it determines, on a case by case basis, how many days of hospitalization can be allocated for a given patient.

Doctors often chafe under the restrictions placed on them as unwarranted and an intrusion on their ability to provide health care. For example, one physician noted that when he started his practice in the 1950s, he would come home with his cash receipts, which his wife would then put in the bank. Now he comes home with two brief cases full of paper work and it may take as long as 90 to 120 days to be paid for services rendered.

This, however, is only one aspect of hospital care which is affecting the hospital's ability to function. A big factor is the ability to provide top quality health care. To achieve this, hospitals are often requiring their key personnel, such as registered nurses, to be certified in their various specialties – obstetrics, emergency care, operating room, and so forth.

According to Mary Toma, Executive Vice President and Chief Operating Officer, "Our Vice President of Patient Care Services has set a goal for her nurses to be certified in their specialties by the year 2000. This holds true of all registered nurses, which means that they have to do whatever it takes to be able to take the test for certification in their specialty. The figure of 300 employees in nursing includes secretaries, nurse aides, operating room technicians, ward secretaries and clerical – but on any given day, we try to keep a 60 to 40 ratio of RN's to non-RN personnel, because of the serious illnesses of our patients."

Ms. Toma points out that currently the hospital is licensed for 200 beds, "but when I began here (in 1974 as Director of Nurses), we had 265 beds operative."

"One of the major changes that I have seen since I began is that when I arrived, one of our big problems was to find the next bed open that could be utilized for the next patient to be admitted."

"The government was compensating hospitals for care provided. It was not too difficult to justify admitting a patient to the hospital. Doctors were admitting patients – and one of our biggest challenges in nursing was to discharge a patient so we could make room for another."

"Today it's just the opposite," she continues. "Our challenge is to increase the number of inpatients. Managed care programs have provided strict guidelines for hospital admissions.

"Today, with the federal government and third party payors reviewing admissions for justification, a patient cannot come to the hospital unless that patient truly needs nursing care," she explains.

"If a patient needs radiology services without nursing care, that patient can obtain this as an outpatient. If a patient needs physical therapy, but not nursing care, the patient only receives physical therapy as an outpatient."

"So, not only a doctor determines that the patient is ill enough to require 24-hour nursing service. Third party payors also have a say as to whether or not a patient can be placed in an acute-care hospital and the hospital reimbursed for their care."

"However," she notes, "the hospital is reviewed on an ongoing basis by the state and federal representatives who determine that patients are not staying in the hospital too long and that they really are admitted appropriately."

"If they find that the patient did not require admission, they will deny payment," she commented. "The patient may have stayed here for weeks, but the hospital may not be paid unless in some instances the physician goes before a hearing board and argues the need for continued hospitalization. This utilization review, as it is called, is becoming stricter all the time and the state and federal government is looking into inappropriate billing for patients from the ancillary services – perhaps lab and radiology departments, or physicians, and the hospital. That's why we have a Utilization Review committee. When the patient comes, before they are admitted, a nurse who is familiar with the criteria for admission works with the admitting department and the physician to assure that the patient is qualified for admission."

"Our current length of stay per patient is 3.5 days," she notes. "When I started, we had a big OB department, we had more than 4,000 deliveries one year which came from our immediate marketing network. The people around the hospital were very young," she explains.

"Over the years, those who have stayed in the community have gotten older, so now we are seeing a higher percentage of Medicare patients than ever and that tends to increase the average length of stay. When a Mom comes in, assuming that all is well, she's in one day and out the next with the baby. When older people come in, they are usually sicker, with more bodily systems involved, so they stay longer. That means, to have an older population of patients, we have to be very careful that our length of stay doesn't become too high."

Ms. Toma further comments that since she started at Norwegian American, the hospital has experienced two acute nursing shortages and that it faces another one in late 1999 or 2000, according to nursing leadership.

"What we are seeing is that many hospitals are offering sign-on bonuses in specialty areas of $4-5,000. Our Vice President of Patient Care Services and I have worked on programs to recruit critical care nurses, the nurse in the critical care nursery, or those in ICU or telemetry, emergency care and even operating room nurses. That's where we are having so many patients admitted to the hospital."

Heading into the 21st century, what are the hospital's strengths? Says Ms. Toma, "Our obstetrics department measures up with the very best in the area and will continue to be so."

"Also, we have a PHO (Physicians Hospital Organization) jointly composed of doctors and representatives of the hospital, and through this joint venture, doctors are better able to become part of managed care organization panels."

The PHO contracts with various managed care programs to provide medical services, Ms. Toma explains. "Some of the HMOs have very strong credentialing requirements. However, when a physician joins our staff and the PHO, chances are increased for that physician to be incorporated on the managed care panels."

Another hospital strength, she observes, is its communications with its medical staff. "We are small enough to be personal and to keep in good touch with our physicians. We in administration attend various medical staff meetings – medical, executive and departmental – and we report on what administration is doing and ask if there's anything they want to share with us, or if they need any new equipment, and so forth. We work very closely with our doctors, realizing that without them we would not have patients."

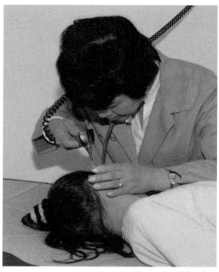

Physician examines ears of a young patient at Hospital Health Fair, one of dozens of such events, held every year.

Then too, she explains, the hospital's community relations program is strong. "I chair a committee called the Community Outreach Committee. We go over all the screenings that we offer the community – including many banks such as Banco Popular, Manufacturers Bank and many others, as well as senior citizens buildings. Hopefully, if they need acute care, they use NAH. The committee is comprised of our manager of community relations, a radiology representative, the Director of the ProHealth satellite clinic operations and myself. We discuss where we can best utilize our outreach resources. From April through November, we have our mobile screening bus to handle health screenings. In winter, we work with the churches, and schools, in offering health screenings inside these facilities."

The Committee works with the Community Trust Fund, another subsidiary of Norwegian American Health Systems, comprised of hospital and community leaders in the areas of banking, government, police, and community and political leaders. Through its own year-round programs, the Fund generates income to cover its various philanthropic activities. Among others, the Fund sponsors the hospital scholarship program which annually offers scholarships to several local youths to enable them to enroll in an accredited healthcare program – pharmacy, nursing, occupational therapy, and so forth. Through the Fund, the hospital also sponsors its own Boy Scout Troop, an explorer troop (for older boys) and a cub pack for younger boys. It is also planning to start a Brownie (Girl Scout) program for younger girls as part of a package of after school activities for community youngsters, which serves as a wholesome and peaceful outlet for their energies.

Another hospital strength, she comments, is its lack of a bureaucracy. "If we need to make a decision we can do it fairly quickly. We have our Board Chairman on site, as well as the president and myself. If someone comes up with a good idea, or if they need some vital piece of equipment, we can move on the request quickly."

Currently the hospital is in the midst of upgrading the entire building interior, remodeling each area, unit by unit. For example, it is remodeling a new intensive care unit since the former ICU was too small, and accordingly, the ICU has been expanded from 8 beds to 12 beds equipped with the latest in technology. In telemetry, the department has grown from 8 to 22 beds, a sign of the hospital responding to today's healthcare needs. Patients entering the hospital today are more acutely ill than in the past.

From the above comments of several key executives, it is apparent that the hospital is at all times attempting to install the latest technological equipment available. It is not a tertiary care center (handling more acutely ill or highly specialized care), nor does it seek to be. It is simply a community hospital and a good one at that, serving its constituents as best as it can. And through its affiliation with Illinois Masonic Hospital, it now has the capability of caring for the acutely ill patients who need specialized care that Norwegian American Hospital cannot provide.

So from almost every perspective – community relations, staff relations, manpower and finances, the hospital is dealing from a hand of strength and experience in meeting the needs of its patient population, and plans to do the best it can in continuing in this fashion for at least the foreseeable future.

Hospital Board of Trustees in one of its regular sessions held several times every year.

EXHIBIT 1

Some Conversations with Those Associated with Norwegian American Hospital Over the Years

Margaret Jensen
– Graduate of the School of Nursing in 1937

I was at the Norwegian American Hospital School of Nursing from 1934 to 1937, and graduated as a nurse in '37. I practiced as a nurse for many years – nearly 50 years in all, teaching and working as assistant director of nurses and I have taught practical nurses, primarily in Georgia and North Carolina. But I also served at both Norwegian American and Lutheran Deaconess, where I finished my training.

While I did my student nursing at Norwegian American, I worked for a while at Lutheran Deaconess Hospital, which was located at Division and Haddon, now St. Mary of Nazareth Hospital.

Our nursing training was tough, believe me. It was a 12 hour stretch from 7:30 a.m. to 7:30 p.m. with classes in between. The same was true for the night shift – from 7:30 p.m. to 7:30 a.m. I was on fourth floor medical. I had 40 patients and we had all kinds of patients. People came to the hospital when they were practically dying in those days.

We had great big canvas oxygen tents that you couldn't even see through and we treated pneumonia with mustard plasters and there was bedrest of 10 days – nobody got out of bed or elevated the bed. This was true of the delivery of babies. You were in the hospital for 10 days and not able to get up until the last. This was before penicillin, so we saw a lot of tragedies.

After graduation I did private duty at various hospitals. I lived in Westmont at the time and moved to the South around 1950. I worked in Georgia and North Carolina in doctors' offices, as a school nurse in the infirmary at Greensboro College in North Carolina.

But the training at Norwegian American Hospital was the best. It was wonderful and very hard – very strict. We had a wonderful relationship with each of the students. I still am in touch with some of them.

Ms. Rosendahl was the director of nurses with her bright red hair. She had been in World War I and – oh brother – I am still frightened when I think of her. She was tough. But those lessons are with me forever. Let's face it. Today there is so little discipline. We had to look sharp with our old-fashioned starched uniforms, and we had better have our shoes shined.

Years later, the only ones that seemed to be dressed as nurses were the private duty nurses. We had white starched uniforms but today we see these students come in slacks and turtle necks and we don't even know who is the head nurse.

We had a very definite pride in our work. It was a great sense of accomplishment, because a lot depended on skilled nursing. Today we don't have that close a patient relationship as we had in those times.

I loved the hospital. Everything was so sparkling. Those old iron beds and the metal desk and dresser. We thought it was wonderful.

I will be 83 in April. I travel extensively. Just got back from Columbus, Ohio where I spoke to 2,300 women at a convention and I am leaving tomorrow morning. I embarked on an entirely new career at age 67 when I started writing and I've written 13 books since and I speak all over the country, at conventions and women's clubs.

We used to have chapel at 6:45 a.m. and Ms. Rosendahl would lead and she loved a certain song and she would always sing it way off key. And we had the most adorable little doll singing. She looked like an angel, but she was really a little rascal. She was the one that snuck out one evening and left the fire escape open. But she was so cute and had a terrific voice.

Then Ms. Rosendahl decided to start a nurse's chorus. And she got a man by the name of Horstmeyer – a great big tall, gangly guy with a long nose. He was going to lead the chorus. She thought he was wonderful, because he would always compliment her on her voice. I will never forget him leading us and we looked like angels, and we didn't dare not to follow his direction. And we would sing the

"Amaryllis – the Beautiful Amaryllis". But it was as though we were tiptoeing through the tulips.

One night when I was in OB, the interns played a terrible trick on me. They painted a great big mustache on me and I couldn't get it off. Patients just loved it. And the interns were only paying me back for a trick that I had played on them. And just then, Ms. Rosendahl told me, "It's time for you to practice, the Lovely Amaryllis." My name was Tweten then. So, I said, "Oh, Ms. Rosendahl, I have a patient here who does not want me to leave." Everyone was doubled up laughing. "You taught me that duty comes first. Much as I want to sing the Lovely Amaryllis, I am going to have to stay here and do my duty." And she told someone else, I could hear her say: "Oh that lovely Ms. Tweten. She is doing her duty as much as she would love to sing. She is staying with her patient."

Those were fun days. I've written several books. Just finished my thirteenth, a book of nursing stories. Many of these are out of print now, but I may try to have some of them published again.

I have three children. My husband died in 1991 and we have six grandchildren, two of whom are in medical school and the others are finishing school.

Of the doctors I worked with, the one I remember best was Dr. Thornton. He was my hero. He used to come to the hospital with a bag of oranges slung over his back. He made rounds early in the morning, around six o'clock and he would bring an orange or a grapefruit to each nurse at her desk to help them get a pickup. He delivered more babies than anyone else at the time.

He was an old-fashioned kind of a doctor. He was a character and you could have written a terrific movie around him. He was so funny. He would come sauntering in with his grapefruit and oranges and he was a great story teller. He would mesmerize the patients and would dish out pink pills and blue pills, all of them out of his pocket but they were only soda.

My mother would bring people to his office. My father was a minister and he helped a lot of poor people and he would tell Dr. Thornton – "Now Dr. Thornton I don't have any money." He was Minister at the Norwegian Baptist Church in Logan Square at the time. My mother would bring the people to Dr. Thornton and she would try to straighten out his desk.

I would sit and swap stories with him. He was a master storyteller. He was my number one memory and I remember Dr. Brewster who taught us Materia Medicus and there were several interns – including a Dr. Helms who was a Methodist minister's son, so we had something in common.

One night, I woke up to find a man in my room. My roommate ordinarily would wake up for anything, but that night she was sleeping like a log. I saw this man and I thought maybe it was one of the interns. They lived on the other side of the hospital and perhaps he had gotten into the wrong room, or might have been out partying a bit too much. Then I could see him more clearly and I yelled out: "Herta – there's a man in the room." She said, "Never mind, I know all about it." She was dreaming about something else. He ran down the stairs and we never did find out who it was. We roused all of the interns out of bed and we got Ms. Rosendahl with her bright red hair piled on top of her head and a great big bathrobe.

We found out that it was not a patient, but a gang of young men outside and we saw someone outside who was telling the other one: "That's the room," and we learned that someone had sneaked out that night and left the fire escape open. We used to leave our door open, but after that we bolted the door and put a chair in front of it. We were terrified. And we would have to go down that long hall to make a telephone call. We had only the one phone. That was a terrifying experience, but we still loved the hospital.

Lorrayne Collamore Jensen – Graduate, School of Nursing 1948

We were the last class where the government paid for our tuition, books and other school expenses for three years. It meant that we did not have to do any military service because the war ended in 1945.

I started nursing school in September 1945. It was a three-year program. There were 30 enrolled in the class and 15 were graduated.

Our day was an 8-hour day which included both classes and floor duty. At the time, because of the war, we were short nurses. It was only about three months from the time we began training until they started to put us on the floors. It was very limited and supervised of course. I thought it was a very good school and a fine hospital. I believe the total tuition at the time for three years was $250. This might seem low today, but it was a lot for the time.

I chose Norwegian because it was near my home and also I had had an appendectomy at Norwegian the year before I finished high school. So I had some familiarity with the hospital.

For many years after I finished nursing school I would say that had I known how hard it was going to be, I would have never gotten into it, but I have never really regretted going into nursing and becoming a registered nurse. It has helped me more than anything else in my entire life.

I was married while in school because at that time they allowed students to get married in their senior year. I have a son and a daughter both born at Norwegian American, who are 48 and 40 respectively.

Two things stand out in my memory about my schooling. First, we had excellent teachers – two primarily, but they guided us and were very good to us and stressed the importance of passing the state board exams. It was a constant reminder of what was to come.

And the other thing about the Norwegian American school of nursing was that it had an excellent reputation and we were affiliated with Cook County Hospital with pediatrics and contagious diseases and we were known as one of the best small schools with a marvelous quality of nursing care. Students that came from Norwegian American always had a good education and were conscientious.

The hard part of the training was that our hours were usually 7 a.m. to 1 p.m. and 4 p.m. to 7 p.m. – there was always a split shift. Those were our hours of work and class. Class might have been from 7 to 9 a.m. or 7 to 8 a.m. and we always had the hardest parts of the day in the p.m. shift.

Then too, some of our nursing school graduates came back, after the war, and were of course supervisors. We had some of the best nurses who supervised and guided us. I had several who were my particular heroines and I strived to achieve that same quality of nursing and caring.

They included Edna Raasach in particular. Jenny Abrahamson was the director when I started and then Mary Jane Thornton followed her. The training and experience that we received were excellent. We were forced to participate in hands on nursing care which was to our advantage rather than being coddled for a long time.

I remember several outstanding doctors. Dr. Lichtenstein was the best in surgery. Dr. Mitchell Nechtow in OB and Dr. B. W. Breister was the godfather of the delivery room.

I worked at Norwegian for eleven years immediately after graduation; then I started to work for Dr. Isoe and I worked for him for 26 years. I left Norwegian in 1959.

What I remember about working at Norwegian was the sense of family. The friendliness. As students we were taught to cooperate and help each other because one student or nurse could not do it all. We all needed some kind of help at one time or another. This was important not only in my professional life, but in my family life as well.

As to the changes, the three-year hospital programs are just about all gone, I think that it's for the best. The nurse today needs more education and training to help her. The field has become so highly technological, that you could not manage with our training. Times have changed. There's no comparison between then and now.

From the time I started in nursing we benefited from all of the advances that were made as a result of the war. Penicillin came out during the time we were students.

New approaches to nursing and medical care evolved as a result of the war that we became a part of. When I first went into training, if a man came in for a hernia, it was not unusual for him to be in bed for two to three weeks. But during the war, they would get patients out of bed a day after surgery. So they never did go back to the old ways.

Roberta Percival
– Student in the school of nursing when it closed in 1962

I started in 1962, the year that the nursing school closed. We had a wonderful school and hospital at the time. I worked for a short time and worked here at Norwegian American Hospital and did private duty for about a year and then I left to raise a family.

But I enjoyed nursing school. It was a life-changing experience. It was a little tougher for us because we were the very last class to be accepted and during that year we had several directors of nursing. That was a problem because they knew that the Board had already decided to close the school and there were three different directors in the period of a year. All of the instructors wanted to leave before the school closed to make sure they could find jobs elsewhere and you couldn't find jobs easily, so you couldn't blame them. They had a very strong alumni group at the time, which has held together over all of these years to this very day.

And I still run the alumni dinners every year – so we did stay together. We have about 30 to 45 who get together for the dinner every year.

We had people who had graduated in the early '40s who were coming to the dinner and were active in the alumni group, while it lasted. We worked and went to school, both. We were only in school for about six to eight weeks when we were already assigned nursing duty in the hospital. So we had a lot of hands on experience. But by the time they got to my class, we were working a regular shift like from 7 a.m. to 3 p.m., the same as today's nurses work, and sometimes from 3 p.m. to 11 p.m. My class never worked the 11 p.m. to 7 a.m. shift. Your day never lasted more than 10 to 12 hours, including class. Some days you would have class for several hours. If you were working evenings, you might have classes all day, but you would not be working.

Capping was six months after you started and you got stripes on your cap during the second year of training and in your third year of training, you had stripes on the side of the cap, and when you were a senior, you had a black stripe the entire width of the cap so you could tell at a glance what year the student nurse was in.

The nurses today probably have more book learning and they make excellent nurses, but it takes a year or two until they have the practical or clinical experience that they need to complete training. They don't have the hands on experience.

The two-year associates degree program is also excellent, but it's been my experience that most of the two-year graduates go on to attend the four year schools and they receive their bachelors degree in nursing.

We ate, slept and worked for the hospital and had to be in by 10 p.m. and there was a house mother who lived in the dorm. My maiden name was Bier.

When you were as close as we were in school, it was great. When we were juniors you could work during your time off and there was a lot of camaraderie.

**Joan Paulov
– Graduate, School of
Nursing, 1957 – who
retired in early 1999
after nearly 42 years
as Nursery Supervisor**

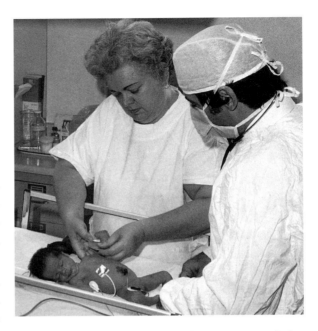

I worked as a charge nurse
in the nursery nights – from
11 p.m. to 7 a.m., for eight
years and then I was pro-
moted to head nurse in the
nursery for the next 28
years, from 1963 to 1991.
Then when they went to a
higher acuity, they needed a
person with more exper-
ience in Level 2, so I was made charge nurse of the regular nursery and the
department supervisor was brought in to handle the special care and regular
nursery.

We could accommodate 40 bassinets in 1957. At the time the nursery, which is
now the playroom on the fourth floor, was the newborn nursery and they had the
beds and rooms and isolettes in the back of the nursery.

Now the capacity is for 45 regular bassinets, 10 intermediate beds and 8
special care. I used to send out letters to the parents after the babies went home
for any twins, triplets that were born at the hospital and they would send pictures
back of the babies. I had an album of all of the babies and the letters from the
parents, so we kept track of the babies. But I just couldn't keep up with it, so it was
discontinued a few years ago.

This was done for all of the babies in intensive care – all of the sick babies.

I have been in this department for more than 41 years but it doesn't seem that
long because we have moved around so much in this department and the science
of taking care of babies has changed so much. Before it was simply that you fed
them with a dropper and you might have to place a tube down their stomach to
give them oxygen if they needed it, but now with all of the monitors – now they

give the babies IV's if they need it and umbilical lines and the whole science is different. It's more complicated. They use ventilators. All of our babies used to be transferred out to perinatal centers so we just stabilized the babies and then they were sent away if they needed special care and treatment. Now about 95 percent of the babies we keep and can care for with all of the equipment that we have.

When I first started, we gave the babies more personal care because the mothers stayed five to seven days each on an average and 10 days for C-Sections, so you got to know the mothers. Now mothers are required to leave in 24 hours usually and there's not much teaching that you can give them in that little time. So there is less of a personal element than when I started.

We were always prepared to handle any emergencies which might arise if we got sick babies. Over the years we have begun to handle more and more high risk babies because of the area in which we are located, but NAH has one of the best records for caring for such sick babies of any hospital in the area.

I don't get involved in the deliveries of the babies except for those that are born by Caesarean Section. And we take a course in neonatal resuscitation every two years to keep us up to date in handling any emergencies that might arise in C-Section babies until they are stabilized and then they are brought into the regular nursery.

We usually have about one or two C-Sections a day. They do these in surgery now. Most of the babies who have traditional births are born in the LDR (Labor, Delivery and Recovery rooms). Now they are going to go to mother-baby, where the babies are going to be sent out to their mothers at the beginning of the year.

At present the babies go back to the nursery in the evening and then they are brought back for visiting hours twice a day from 2 to 4 p.m. and from 7 to 8 p.m., and the babies are returned here and observed through the nursery.

When I leave, I think I will miss the camaraderie of the people I have worked with over the years. The hospital has been very friendly and homelike. It's been good to me. We've had good rapport with the doctors. I've always gotten along with them.

When I first started the patients were all Polish, Jewish and Norwegian and now they are black and hispanic. Also, the care is more routine now. They go home so fast. You have to do certain things in certain hours and they have to make certain they meet certain criteria before we discharge them. This is required now for all patients. It used to be that way anyhow for private patients also, but now a law has been passed which says that they can't force you to be discharged in 24 hours. You can stay 48 hours if you want to. Most of patient insurance however is still geared to a discharge of the mother and the baby after 24 hours, with an early discharge clinic in which the mother and baby come back the following day or the day after that for a final examination.

We had quadruplets once and they left the hospital alive, but they were very tiny and they died within a few days. But we've had a couple of sets of triplets and lots of twins.

Now that I am retiring, I love to garden. I have a home in Libertyville with a big lawn and my Mom is living with me and she's 85, so she's one of the reasons that I am retiring so that I can take care of her.

I don't think I'll give up nursing completely. I'll probably work once a month or so. But the commuting to and from Libertyville is tough – it's 35 miles each way.

We used to live much closer to the hospital, but I moved out to Libertyville in 1975. Requirements for working in the nursery are much stricter today. Nowadays you need all sorts of special courses to be certified in neonatology (care of the newborns).

When we went through school at Norwegian American, we only paid $100 tuition for all three years and that included food and lodging. But we worked for our service. We'd go to school during the day and by the time we were seniors or graduates, we were already in charge of wards. So after we graduated, we were charge nurses. I worked nights as a charge nurse. We had a lot of experience.

We had 17 in my class. Most of my classmates are retired now. Three live in California, two in Indiana, one in Tennessee, two in Wisconsin and they are spread out all over. When the hospital celebrated its Centennial a few years ago, our class all returned for a reunion. We had 12 of the 17 back and it was nice.

In our second and third years, we rotated through the various hospital departments. Now the nurse goes to college and they have the theoretical knowledge, but they need a lot of experience in the wards. Now nursing school is very expensive. It's so expensive that many of our girls and young men simply can't afford it.

Ruth Pedersen
– Nursing Exchange Student in 1952 under
the American Scandinavian Foundation

I came to Norwegian American Hospital as an exchange nurse under the American Scandinavian Foundation Program, arriving in August 1952, and remained here for additional training for two years.

I then returned home to Norway and came back to the hospital in May 1955 and remained there for a total of fourteen and a half years. I worked first in a general medical-surgical wing on the third floor and then went to the Operating Room where I worked the rest of my career at Norwegian American.

I vividly recall many of the doctors involved in the Operating Room at the time. There was Dr. Lichtenstein and Dr. Nechtow and Dr. Colletti and Dr. Giosh, and the two Fowlers, Frank and John. Then there was Dr. Murphy, a very fine gentleman, and Dr. Rudnick, who was in charge of urology, and Dr. Dale Rold, who was a very fine doctor. I remember them all. And there was Dr. Lieberman in ophthalmology. I still see him. And Dr. Cavenagh in cardiology and Dr. Ahstrom in orthopedics and Dr. Verhaag. I still exchange Christmas cards with Marge Del Rosso.

When I first came to the hospital as an exchange student, I was sent here from Norway. I then worked for the State of Illinois Read Hospital where I was in charge of the Operating Room for many years.

I came from a big hospital in Oslo to little Norwegian American and it was quite a change. I made a few boo-boos until I caught on. For instance, I was boiling catheters and other instruments in a large container, which was the way we did it in Norway, but I didn't know that they had sterilizing equipment for this purpose.

It was a good little hospital and the atmosphere was very good. They had a nursing school that was something that the hospital could be proud of. We had as many as 18 exchange students here while I was in the nursing exchange program. There was one young lady from Sweden, and a few Icelanders and several Danes, but mostly Norwegians.

This was a program that was initiated by Mr. Faleide, who I believe was the board chairman at the time. The hospital really took us under their wings. They were marvelous. But the program ended after the two years that I worked in the hospital. There were no new students after that.

Compared to other hospitals, Norwegian American may have been a little old-fashioned, but it was nice. There was a fantastic togetherness among all people who worked there. It was like we were all members of one big family.

Because of the numerous calls that we took in the Operating Room; we had little time for any outside activities. Dorothy Taylor was in charge of the Operating Room when I first started. Later we got Ms. Jerry Hempleman, who was old-fashioned and very strict.

The patients were of all different nationalities. When I first came, I had been in the Operating Room only about two weeks and we had a patient, a very nice old lady who asked me: "How long have you been in this country?" and I told her that I had come only a fortnight ago. Seven years later I found myself in a card shop looking for a particular card and this little old lady standing next to me said: "Did you ever work at Norwegian American Hospital as a nurse?" I replied, "Yes," and she said, "I never forgot you because you told me that you came only a fortnight ago."

When the hospital had its Centennial celebration several years ago, I was invited to a special luncheon and I couldn't believe how nice it looked – everything was spotless and there was park all around. I couldn't recognize my old Operating Room which was already in its new quarters.

Magnhild Faland
– Nursing exchange student under the
American Scandinavian Foundation program in 1952

I was at Norwegian American Hospital for about two years starting in November 1952. And then I returned to Norway to get my immigration papers. I was married in Norway in November 1954 and returned to Norwegian American in April 1955.

I worked at Norwegian for about a year and then I left because we moved to Norridge. I then worked for two pediatricians and as O.R. supervisor at Belmont Hospital for many years. Then I worked for the Chicago Read Hospital which was run by the State of Illinois. At that time they had medical and surgical units and I was hired to supervise the Emergency Room and the medical supplies. I worked there with another exchange student from Norway who had trained at Norwegian American – Mrs. Pedersen, who was the supervisor of the Operating Room.

My training at Norwegian American helped a lot. We learned to perfect our English, for one. My English was not good when I first came. I worked in surgery there and I enjoyed every minute of it.

I remember Dr. Lichtenstein of course and Dr. Rold and Dr. Isoe and the Danish Dr. Jensen. I remember all of them. And I keep in touch with the woman who was the O.R. supervisor then – Jerry Hempleman. Then there was old Jenny Jensen. She was a character and absolutely needed. She was in charge of cleaning up and getting the instruments ready for surgery – sort of a nurse aide. She would say what she meant.

I have some very fine memories of the hospital and am thankful that I was fortunate to work in surgery at the time. I had very little surgical experience before.

Now I am retired but I am involved in a lot of activities within the Scandinavian Association so I keep very busy and then I have two sons and three grandchildren and that takes care of my time.

Lorraine Becker Wavruk
– Graduate, School of Nursing, 1957

I was one of five sisters, four of whom graduated from the Norwegian American School of Nursing – my two older sisters graduated in the '40s, I finished in '57 and my other sister graduated in '65.

My oldest sister, Violet, had a classmate in Wisconsin – we're from Manitowac – and her best friend was Laverne Gustavson, and she had gone to Norwegian American School of Nursing – she was of Norwegian descent – and that's how we happened to get to that school. During the war, Violet worked as a cadet nurse. My sister Betty finished in '49. I finished in '57. It was a three-year program at the time. My sister Eloise started in '60, but the school was closed in '62, so she finished her training at South Chicago Community Hospital. All of the schools were closing at the time, or so it seemed.

After finishing school, I went into the Air Force and was there for several years. I came out as a captain in the Air Force Nurses Corps. Then I came back to Chicago and took a job in the operating room at Norwegian American Hospital.

Dr. Vicari was chief of surgery at the time and he was looking for a nurse and this was in '65. I was at Norwegian until '67 and then I went to St. Mary of Nazareth as the private nurse of Dr. Vicari for 26 years. And when he retired in '89, I continued working in the operating room and took a job at West Suburban Hospital. And I've been there about ten years.

My other sisters are all alive. Three are retired, one due to illness, and my sister Eloise is working in Green Bay. Betty Jane lives in River Forest and retired at age 65 just a couple of years ago after working as Dr. Knudson's private nurse. And Violet, my oldest sister, went back to Manitowac after graduation and worked there until '65. She would still be working had not the hospital closed and she did not want to start at another hospital.

Norwegian was my home away from home because I was 18 years old and we all lived at the dormitory. At the time, our dormitory was where the cafeteria is today. It seemed like a family. All of the nursing school directors were very nice – very professional. They all wore uniforms, caps. As far as our education goes, it was professional.

All of my career, I have been complimented and people have asked where did you get your training. Because in those days, you did a lot of studying in nursing school and we did a lot of practical work as well. So we had not only the theoretical, but the practical too. The chief surgeon at West Suburban just commented today that they don't make nurses like they used to. So, I've worked as a nurse for 41 years and I still hold down two jobs. I still work at Norwegian part-time and they were looking for help about nine years ago. I would go there in the afternoon and work until about 9 p.m. and then I would take Saturdays and stay there. But I loved it. It was never a job.

At Norwegian, we would get two weeks off during the summer so, except for that, the training continued the year-round and we worked different shifts. We went to school during the daytime and worked on the floors from 3 p.m. to 11 p.m. or from 11 p.m. to 7 a.m. and then my classes would run from 8 a.m. to 3 p.m. and I would then go to my room and try to get some sleep. Weekends we had off and usually I would work to help out my parents by earning some additional money.

While I was a student we had a fantastic staff of doctors – there was Dr. Giosh, and Dr. Jensen, Dr. Lichtenstein and Dr. Ahstrom, who was an orthopedic surgeon, and his father was a general surgeon. I worked with the son at West Suburban later on. And there was Dr. Triolo and Dr. Bartkus and the Fowlers – the list just goes on and on. Some were General Practitioners and performed minor surgeries. There was Dr. Nechtow in OB-Gyn and Dr. Rold, a very find obstetrician and in orthopedics there were the Ahstroms and a Dr. Verhaag and some of the general surgeons even did orthopedics in those days, like Dr. Jensen. Then there was Dr. Page who worked with me.

My sister Elvera keeps in touch. All I can say is that it was a very nice place to work. For me to leave home when I was 18, it was a good place and they took good care of us. I learned a lot there.

I should mention that I took part in the choir and sang with the hospital sextet at Field's during the Christmas holidays. Mary Jane Norton was the nursing director at the time.

Norine Fleischhacker
– Graduate, School of Nursing, 1959

I worked at County Hospital for five years after finishing my schooling at Norwegian. I worked at Norwegian then for a few months until my second son was born here and then I returned to the hospital in May of 1965 and have been working here ever since.

I have ten children, all of whom were born at Norwegian except for the last two.

When I first returned to the hospital in 1965, I used to work part-time as a float nurse and then I was promoted to relief in-house supervisor and I was transferred to the emergency room about eight years ago, where I work the night shift.

I was here when the neighborhood was changing. There were 15 in my class but a few dropped out and we ended up with 10 in the class that graduated. Ms. Nordahl was the director of the nursing school and she was preceded by Ms. Allman.

Primarily, I chose to go to Norwegian American for my nursing training because the tuition was very low – it was only about $100 at the time for three years, and money was tight. I worked part-time as a nurse aide at St. Mary of

Nazareth and at that time they wanted $250 for nursing school, so I looked around for another hospital in the neighborhood. My parents lived at North Avenue and Rockwell at the time so it was very close to Norwegian American.

After completing my training at Norwegian and passing my state boards, I worked as a nurse in the emergency room at County Hospital for about two and a half years – and I became head nurse in the female surgical unit and left after my older son was born in '63. I worked for a few months in Norwegian until the birth of my second son and returned again the following May.

I remember that there was a lot of unrest in the neighborhood primarily of a political nature and when the union tried to come into the hospital in the early '70s, that was a problem. But the people were nice and I remember that they would admit people into the emergency room that didn't have any insurance. It made no difference to them. This is certainly true today, where we take everyone that comes into the emergency room regardless of their ability to pay.

I will be 61 very shortly and I hope that I will be able to continue for at least another few years since I still have children in school. So I do the best I can with what I have to offer, even though you can't please everyone all of the time.

As an emergency room nurse, here at Norwegian, we have to take the advanced cardiac life support program so that your credentials are proper and this has to be done every two years – in other words, you can't just sit back and relax once you are certified. And then there's pediatric life support credentials which you are required to have to be credentialed in emergency room nursing.

Norwegian has a lot of pleasant memories to offer. Now we can offer full-time physician staffing in the emergency room at any time, day or night.

Josephine Nordahl Ray
– Director, School of Nursing in 1957

I was director of nursing for several years in the mid-'50s and also director of the school of nursing and a graduate of the school in '37. I worked there for a year in the operating room and then left to go into public health and then became associated with the Visiting Nurses.

In the operating room, Catheryn Williams was the supervisor and also Regina Jensen was working there and she was another graduate of the school. She died a few years ago. She and I were on call every other day. We would go to work at 7 p.m. and were on call until 7 a.m. the following day – every other day. We were often on call – there was a good deal of work on call.

Then I worked for about four years with the Visiting Nurses Association. After that, I went back to school and got my degrees in nursing education – bachelors and masters. I then returned to the hospital for several years and left there in '42. I will be 84 next month.

After I received my degrees, I worked for the Chicago Board of Education and got a teaching certificate to teach practical nursing in high school and I was assigned to teach practical nursing to the girls at Lucy Flower High School. Then I went to the Oak Park Hospital School of Nursing where I became educational director and finally director of the school of nursing and nursing service and was there during the '40s for about 12 years. They closed the school of nursing when the nursing programs were being expanded to the colleges.

I then retired and needed something to do and took an industrial nursing job at the old Stewart Warner plant and worked there for four years until 1980 when I married Mr. Ray.

We then moved to Palm Beach and I did volunteer work at the Palm Beach Blood Bank – that was the last nursing that I did.

I recall working as a student nurse for Mrs. Bevoe in the Pharmacy. We had pharmacy duty and I counted out the pills and delivered them to the patients.

We were on duty from 7 p.m. to 7 a.m. with a few hours off if you weren't busy. And classes were held during the daytime. The Nursing program was for three years, which it remained until it closed in 1962.

After I left the hospital and went on to get a degree and other positions, I kept in touch with Marge Del Rosso and Regina Jensen who continued working at the hospital until she was about 80 and lived until she was 96 and died at the Norwegian Home for the Aged.

I remember Dr. Anton Jensen very well. He did a lot of surgery and Regina would always make certain that he was dressed properly for surgery. I also remember Helga Ruud, who was semi-retired at that time, who taught us OB. And there was Dr. Warren Johnson, who was considered the macho man of surgery and who was a powerhouse in the operating room and I scrubbed for him a few times. And there was Dr. Lichtenstein, a very fine gentleman. I had great respect for him. He was an excellent surgeon.

I recall that there were always staff meetings for the doctors where they would always discuss some topic of importance and the nurses could attend some of these meetings – they were held at 10 or 11 a.m. followed by lunch. The hospital was about 250 beds at the time.

Leona Messer was the director of nursing when I finished nursing school in '37 and Hattie Bell Travis was the director before her. Ms. Rosendahl was the night supervisor when I was in school. She was up in years and was from Stoughton, Wisconsin and she was very strict – as much so when I was the director as when I was student. She was a great lady.

When we were students, we all had to go to chapel every morning before we went on duty and we had to be there at 6:45 a.m. and we would have a chapel service, sing two hymns and the Lord's Prayer, and then we had breakfast and went to work. One of my classmates, Esther Dahl, played the piano for chapel. She was a former school teacher before she came to nursing school.

Marge Del Rosso
– Archivist at Norwegian American Hospital, formerly Medical Staff Secretary and Secretary to the Director of Nursing

I came to the hospital in 1956 when I answered an ad for secretary to the Director of Nursing who at the time was Mrs. Irene Allman. She was also connected with the school of nursing and I worked with the educational director of the school of nursing and Mrs. Allman for several years and then she left to become nursing director at St. Mary of Nazareth Hospital and as far as I know she is still there. She has been one of their top administrators all of these years.

There were several directors in the school of nursing after that, but I didn't remain as secretary for too long. I enjoyed the work and I enjoyed the students. I recall the capping ceremonies vividly. That was a big event in their lives and was held after they had been there for so many months – they had to earn their caps and there was a big ceremony. And when they graduated they would take the state boards and they became Registered Nurses and we would have graduation exercises and they could practice as RN's. It was a three-year diploma program.

I was there until the school closed in 1962 and I kept all of the student nurses records. They were wonderful years. The school occupied the second and third floors of what was then the new building at the southwest end of Richmond and Cortez and the second and third floors were built to house the school of nursing. When the school closed, they used the space for patient rooms, but we had 60 students when the building was brand new and then the main floor of that corner of the hospital housed the house mother's office and the receptionist where parents or visitors could come. It was a beautiful reception area and was decorated by Carson Pirie Scott, which was the work of the then Women's Auxiliary President, who was I believe Edna Hansen.

Students came from all over including one from Hawaii and from Stoughton, which was a Norwegian town in Wisconsin. Not all of them were of Norwegian ancestry, but a good many were. And they received a very well rounded education for the money. They got their clinical practice with patients right there at the hospital. Later on, when the collegiate programs took over, the students had the theory but lacked the clinical experience which they got at our nursing school, so they would have to obtain that clinical experience after they left college.

After the school closed in '62, I was in medical education and my job was to recruit interns and residents from the foreign countries – the Philippines and India, and Iran and a few from Turkey, Korea and from all over. There were a few from Norway as well – who were here before I started to work in the medical education program. They were here as part of the American Scandinavian program and these were interns and residents who came from Norway or Sweden. And I recall several physical therapists from Holland – very good ones – who remained here for a long time. I helped to set up many of these medical education programs while I was still working in nursing.

I moved around quite a while after the school closed and was in personnel for a time.

Norine Fleischhacker, a graduate of our school of nursing is a night nurse in the Emergency Room and still works here. She has many children, nearly all of them were born right here at Norwegian American. Her husband is a fireman with the Chicago Fire Department.

In medical education, I remember, we had clinics on Saturday mornings and sometimes we would have 50 people attending on the second floor and I would help to set up the chairs – we had a medical and a surgical and a tumor clinic. It was on the second floor where the lab is located now and my office was in back of the lab. Dr. Lichtenstein and Dr. Page, an orthopedic surgeon, would see these patients before surgery and then they would come in as outpatients and would see the patients after surgery and this went on all Saturday morning. The tumor clinics started just before I came and medical records was next to my office.

Perhaps the thing that I recall of great historical significance was the Memorial Plaques. Part of my duties as medical staff secretary was to order the plaques for this Memorial after a doctor would pass away. This was headed by Dr. Proud who was a family practitioner and a wonderful man. His wife, like all of the wives of the doctors there, was very active in the Auxiliary. All the doctors brought their patients there, and their wives became members of the Auxiliary and they had a lot of interest in the hospital. Their husbands worked here of course and they got to know one another quite well. So we had husbands and wives working for the good of the hospital.

I remember the significance of the Memorial plaques, since Dr. Fenger was the first doctor to be memorialized with a plaque, followed by Dr. Hektoen. The Memorial was always kept on the first floor and would literally stop people in their tracks. It is currently in the first floor medical library adjacent to the doctors' lounge and it's accessible to the doctors. I am not certain how many plaques are displayed on the Memorial but I remember that Dr. Lombardo was the last one to have a plaque displayed there.

This Honor Roll lasted through World War II and when there were only two places left, I would be kidded by the doctors who would tell me that they did not want to have their names added. I told them that they would not see their names on it. I thought that this was a nice way to honor the doctors.

Dr. Robins, who was here in the '60s and who was from Arkansas, had interned at Norwegian American in '27 so the doctors knew him. When he sold his practice, he became Director of Medical Education here. Dr. Murphy took over as Director of Medical Education after Dr. Robins died.

Then I was secretary to the medical staff for many years. Also I worked in EKG (electrocardiagram), and I was secretary to Dr. Cavenagh. I was doing EKG and I was still doing a lot of the medical staff secretarial duties. I was doing all the committee and staff meetings.

I recall Dr. Helen Button very well. She was quite active here and she was a surgeon also on the staff of Thorek Hospital. And there was Dr. Victoria Elliot, who was a very fine family practitioner and later became the head of the medical staff.

Also, there was Dr. Larsandrew Dolan who was here for many years and was also the Director of the Norwood Park Home. We had doctors who represented the various ethnic communities in the area at the time – we had Jewish doctors, Polish doctors and Italian doctors – quite an assortment – and they all got along very well and this was true of the Women's Auxiliary as well.

The Norwegian influence was on the decline as far as the medical staff was concerned, but we still had some Norwegian employees. There were three, formerly four, on the hospital board who were of Norwegian Ancestry – Art Bagge, recently retired, Perry Gulbrandsen, Chris Johansen, also retired, the Vice Chairman of the Board and Norman Dahl, former Chairman of the Board.

Comparing those days when I started with current times, there have been many changes – the medical staff has changed, the patients have changed and medicine itself has changed. But I have always felt right from the start that NAH was a very friendly hospital and it still is. It's like family. The people here are easy to get to know. And considering the assortment of people that are on staff here, everyone gets along just fine

Edith DeYoung
– Former administrative secretary to several hospital administrators and administrative assistant to the Immediate Past President/CEO as well as the former Chairman of the Board, Norman R. Dahl

I started at the hospital in 1963 as a receptionist handing out visitor passes and answering phone inquiries regarding patient rooms, etc., taking care of newspaper orders, as well as managing all incoming and outgoing mail for the hospital. In 1963, NAH did not have a mail room. There was no Security Department as there is today. Kane and Central Watch Security personnel were used by the hospital to provide the service.

During the late 1960s, the hospital was a 264-bed full-to-capacity facility. An extensive remodeling program was desperately needed. At this time, the cafeteria was located on the first floor where the administrative offices are now housed. The x-ray department as well as a small emergency room were also located on the first floor and there was no Nursing Unit 2-A (this area was used as Interns and Residents quarters). Many employees lived in an apartment building across the street, where the medical office building stands today.

In the early 1970s, the hospital established its own security department and hired Edward Pedziwater as its director. Personnel were hired specifically for this department and through an extensive training program became certified by the Police Department to carry weapons. The receptionist area was incorporated into this department thus bringing me into this newly-established department. Men and women officers wore white shirts, blue pants, skirts, badges and those certified, carried weapons. My position then changed to include the tasks of keeping the officers informed of any problems via an intercommunications system, as the officers use today.

The man who developed my love for NAH during these early years was Trustee Art Bagge, recently retired from the Board of Trustees. He is a most loving and gracious man who treated all employees with respect and friendliness. Little did I know that I would be working with the Board of Trustees and Trustee Art for many years to come.

In the late 1970s a secretarial position became available in Administration. Richard Sellers was then administrator and Ann Schwab had been promoted from secretary to assistant to the administrator. The administrative area at the time consisted of three rooms: the administrator's office, the assistant's office and the office of the secretary.

In 1982 the Board of Trustees felt it necessary to bring in a management company. Mr. William Leyhe, of National Medical Enterprises, out of California, was brought in to run the hospital. As part of Mr. Leyhe's strategy, he relocated several adjoining department offices (then Personnel and Housekeeping) and established an administrative suite of offices and hired and promoted various individuals to top management positions (vice presidents, an operating officer, assistant to the administrator and PR/Marketing director). Mr. Leyhe, with the approval of the Board Chairman, established the annual Board of Trustees' retreat, still taking place today. He held weekly management meetings. He critiqued everything as well as everyone working in a management position. Many new and innovative programs and projects were initiated during his era.

When Bill Leyhe accepted a promotion within the company, responsibility for administering the day-to-day activities of the hospital was given to Michael Sussman, of Brim & Associates, a subsidiary of National Medical Enterprises. Mr. Sussman served as administrator for several years after which Brim offered him another position. The hospital was then without a chief executive officer for more than a year. In the interim, Norman R. Dahl, Chairman of the Board of Trustees, with the assistance of the senior management staff, took over the hospital operations. Also during this period the Board conducted an extensive search for a CEO.

Failing to find a suitable candidate, the Board concluded that the hospital was strong financially and had a top management team and felt that the hospital could be managed from within. Clarence Nagelvoort was appointed President/CEO.

Having served four administrators, my final and most exciting experience with NAH was to serve as administrative assistant to the Chairman of the Board, Norman R. Dahl. Not only was it a pleasure to work with him, I consider him my friend. From preparing Board retreats to preparing for the visit of the King and Queen of Norway, the office ran at a high energy level. It was my privilege to attend and take minutes for the parent corporation, NAH Board of Trustees, NAH Foundation, NAH Community Trust, Executive Committee, Viking Ball Committee, and medical missions meetings. I will always fondly remember the members of these committees and boards as well as all the great physicians I have come to know and respect over the years. I firmly believe that the hospital would not have prospered without Mr. Dahl's direction and leadership. I truly can say I have been in the presence of greatness.

Over my 32 years of service, I have seen a constant shuffling and reshuffling of space as new departments were installed without any corresponding expansion of the physical plant. I have been privileged to see the construction of the new surgical suite, pediatric area, a new OB wing, expansion of the Emergency Room, new Promenade, parking lots, opening up of the campus area, and many many more projects and activities. I have also been privileged to have sat in on the architect's meetings for the newly-constructed Medical Office Building and to see at least a part of the construction taking place on this magnificent building.

In May 1996, due to my husband's health, we retired to Mountain Home, Arkansas, a small community in the Ozark Mountains. One son lives in Bourbonnais, Illinois and the other in California, so our traveling does bring us back to Illinois once in a while. My faithful friends at NAH keep me up on the news of NAH, which I always look forward to. I have taken Norman Dahl's words with me, "remember, CHALLENGES MAKE US GROW!"

Dr. John Cavenagh – Retired physician who was on the medical staff from 1952-1993 and on the Board of Trustees from 1979-1989

I was with Norwegian American Hospital for 41 years, from 1952 to 1993. Through the 1970s and into the '80s we weathered declining hospital business. Activity began to pick up in the 1980s.

The neighborhood had changed from a middle European area – it had been largely Jewish when I first joined the staff and then mid-European later on and then gradually began to turn Latino in the '70s. With the hospital's primarily Latino and Filipino medical staff, we were able to capitalize on that change in our population. And the hospital became recognized as the neighborhood hospital for the Spanish speaking people. Before we turned to National Medical Enterprises for their help in running the hospital, there was a crisis in the late '60s and in the early '70s in which the Board of Trustees and the medical staff debated whether to abandon the hospital and to move out to the Northwest suburbs in Park Ridge in an area which was subsequently taken over by Lutheran General. It was decided at that time that we would stay here and that we would serve as the hospital for the Humboldt Park Community. So this issue was agreed upon and settled and there was no further discussion on it.

At the beginning of the '80s, management changes came in the hospital operation. We looked in general at management companies and wound up signing a contract with National Medical Enterprises and they appointed Mr. Bill Leyhe to run the hospital. He turned out to be an outstanding administrator – one of the best we have ever had.

But he left and was replaced by Mr. Sussman, who was also an excellent administrator and did a good job. Then Clarence Nagelvoort, who recently left, came to us from Presbyterian-St. Luke's Hospital, first as Pharmacy Director, and later as administrator proved to be a very competent administrator.

In the three or four years that I have retired from the hospital, the entire medical industry has undergone such earthshaking changes that it's hard to say with any degree of certainty where the industry is heading. What I call the corporatization of medical practice and hospital care has made such a radical change in American medicine that it's hard to tell where it will all end up.

During most of the 41 years that I was on the staff, the Board did not have very close relationships with the medical staff. The medical staff ran its own affairs and the Board theirs and there was little contact between them. But in recent years there has been more interplay between the Board and the medical staff and as you may know, I was Vice Chairman of the Medical Staff for several years and I was on the Board from 1979 to '89.

The relations between the various members of the medical staff over the years were warm. It was a nice staff to be on. It was a very close knit staff. I remember Dr Mitchell Nechtow was attending physician at County Hospital while I was in training at County. I spent four years there in training. Dr. Nechtow and Dr. Rudnick, a urologist, were close friends and worked at County as well as at Norwegian. And the Fowlers – Frank Sr. and his two sons – Frank and John – were very prominent physicians at Norwegian American. Frank Jr. was President of the Chicago Medical Society for a year.

I also remember Dr. Ralph Warden. He was our first radiologist and was still head of radiology when I joined the staff in 1952. He had one of the first x-ray diagnostic units in the city of Chicago and Dr. Harold Sofield came to Norwegian American in the early 1920s to do orthopedic work. He did some of the first hip pinnings in the Chicago area.

They had the x-ray machine and the staff was very prominent in the early part of the century. Dr. Hektoen was still here and Dr. Lichtenstein, who came a little later, was a great surgeon. He usually wrote number one on the Cook County Hospital competitive examination in surgery. There was also Dr. Halstead and Dr.

Anton Carlson, from the University of Chicago, so we had a marvelous history, especially in those early years.

It was originally the Norwegian Lutheran Tabitha Hospital and the deaconesses ran the hospital and then some of the Board members didn't want the deaconesses any more and they split off and some of the deaconesses formed Lutheran Deaconess which was the forerunner of the present Lutheran General Hospital in Park Ridge.

There were wonderful things that happened over the years at the hospital. We started doing peritoneal dialysis and we trained nurses to read EKG's and to do intensive care nursing and cardiac resuscitation and that sort of thing. Yes, we had many things to be proud of at Norwegian American Hospital.

Dr. Michael Colletti
– Retired physician who was on the
medical staff from 1937 to 1986

I was born in Southern Illinois, near Duquoin and Marion, and we moved to Chicago when I was 12 and I didn't finish grade school until I was 16. I went to Crane High school one summer to make up one year, so I finished high school in three years. While in high school, we didn't have a track coach and my teacher entered me in a track meet at Soldier Field in the 100- and 200-yard dash. I really didn't want to compete in these events since I had never practiced them, but I entered anyhow and I qualified and there were eight runners in the event. That was on a Wednesday and on Saturday the final was held and I won the 100-yard dash in 1928 and the next day the *Tribune* headline read: "Unknown from McKinley (my high school) Pushes Through to Win the 100-yard Dash." Later at Loyola, I was on the track team and ran against such great athletes as Ralph Metcalf, who went on to win the Olympics. But that was many years ago.

I retired from the medical staff 12 years ago. I am a general practitioner and my office was located at Grand and Oakley for many years and the hospital was especially convenient for me.

I knew two doctors particularly well at Norwegian: Dr. Anthony Triolo, who introduced me to Dr. Frank Fowler Jr., one of the two sons of Dr. John Fowler, who was still practicing at the hospital at that time.

I recall in particular the nursing staff when I joined the staff. That's when they all wore caps and gowns and you knew a nurse was a nurse. I often would give lectures to the nurses.

I was married in 1940 and entered the service during World War II in 1942. At that time my practice was not large, but when I got out of the service, I started to accept public aid patients and there were many children who were ill and their parents could not afford to pay the doctor. I remember that I would make about $25 a month working four hours every Wednesday. Eventually, that increased to $50 but that was when things were really tough.

But when I returned from the War, the nurses started sending me a lot of patients and I became involved in obstetrics and I probably delivered more babies than the obstetricians. I took care of the entire family – children and grownups and I made house calls.

We used to run into a lot of sore throats and high temperatures and everyone was afraid of polio. I ran into a lot of that. My patients were of all different nationalities. Polio was a big killer before they discovered the polio vaccine. That came along much later.

Later, I moved into a large building with a drug store and a laboratory and with several doctors and dentists at Chicago and Western Avenues – that was in the late '50s. I used to visit the various schools in the area and would examine the children there.

I particularly remember two cases. I was in the office and asked Ms. Scroggins if I could admit a woman who was very ill and needed surgery and I told her that I would be glad to take care of her. This was during the Depression. This was after I had been connected with the hospital for some time. I probably had more patients admitted at Norwegian American than any other doctor at the time.

I talked to the administrator and he called me in and the woman was middle aged and she had gall stones, and he told me that it would be okay to admit her.

Later I got permission to admit another poor patient, who had surgery performed by Dr. Triolo. Again the hospital extended itself for this woman. In both cases there was no charge by either me or the hospital. They were wonderful in both of these cases.

Later on, I joined the staff at Oak Park Hospital, but I didn't do too much there.

I used to do a lot of tonsilectomies for children sent to me by the Infant Welfare Society. This is how my practice began to grow. I used to take night calls. Any time the patient felt that they needed to talk to me, I never refused to talk to them. Today, you often don't even know who your doctor is.

Many times I would see a patient fumbling around in their purse for change to pay me and they would need a prescription and I would call up the pharmacist and tell him: "Pat, don't charge this woman," and I would take care of it.

I have one son who's an oral surgeon who lives in Aurora and another in sales who's doing very well and a daughter who is president of a bank in Ohio.

I remember Dr. Warden, our x-ray department head, and what a wonderful person he was. There was one incident that I recall involving a patient who had a fractured wrist and he went ahead and took the x-rays and he gave me instructions on what to do – how to set the bone so that it would heal. And I remember Dr. Proud – what a gentleman. And Dr. Lombardo was there at the time.

I grew up in the neighborhood of Leavitt and Ohio Streets and at that time it was largely Irish and Polish and quite close to the hospital.

Just recently my wife passed away and there was one lady who approached me at the wake and she hugged me and I looked at her and she asked me: "Do you know why I am here?" It turned out that I had delivered all three of her children, who are grown up now, of course. She was so happy to see me and she said: "I remember all of the days that you took care of us, and we miss you very much."

I have many wonderful memories of the hospital. Everyone helped each other. Dr. Triolo and I started an annual get-together of staff doctors and wives around 1950 and that later became the Viking Ball around 1962.

We used to have golf tournaments and lectures for the doctors at least once a week. Everyone would take a turn in giving the lectures. We tried to get every doctor on the staff to discuss whatever subject they wanted to talk about. And it was harmonious all the way through.

I remember when our Pathologist – Dr. Learner – retired, we interviewed two candidates for the job. One was our present pathologist – Dr. Campanini who had trained at Michael Reese Hospital. And the other was a tall Irish fellow and we were about 13 at the table representing different specialties. After interviewing, we voted and it was a tie. I was the odd man and I went with Dr. Campanini knowing full well where he had come from. And I broke the tie in his favor and he turned out to be one of the best pathologists we have ever had.

When I started out in '37, general practitioners did everything. I recall a Dr. Lieberman, an ophthalmologist, who later went to Resurrection Hospital.

I remember another incident where a patient came in for a hernia repair and after surgery, he started bleeding and I was wondering what this was about and I called over Dr. Lichtenstein and after examining the patient, he said that this patient had been acting up and had tried to get out of bed and had loosened up a suture and as a result had started to bleed. The patient threatened to sue me, but it all wound up alright.

I should also mention that when I was on Chicago and Western, if Dr. Triolo or any of the other doctors in the building – there were six or seven of us – wanted to go on vacation, we would take care of each other's patients. And we would turn over all funds collected for treating each other's patients. This worked beautifully and we could take it easy knowing that our patients would receive good medical care.

William Lichtenstein
– Son of the late Manuel Lichtenstein, prominent surgeon on Norwegian American Hospital's medical staff, 1935-71

It's hard for me to talk about my father as remarkable, but he was in many ways a very unique, unusual person. He was a tough guy born at a time when his parents had to move about frequently because they had no money. His father died when he was 18 – they were immigrants. My Dad was born in 1900 around the area of California and Ohio, not far from Norwegian American Hospital.

We grew up in a building around Division and Kedzie, and we never really moved from there. When Dad was just a little boy, he was selling newspapers on a corner not far from where they lived. He never wanted to talk about this. His mother and father rolled cigarettes for a living. They had a little shop where they shaved people. It was open from morning until night. They had several kids and when his father died, he could get to the funeral only by streetcar. They had no money.

How he ever got through medical school was a minor miracle. He worked constantly. He taught. He was a principal employee. He worked in the post office. He managed to get through the University of Chicago and even joined the army in World War I. But he got his medical degree from Rush Medical School at the University of Chicago. He was not involved in World War I because it ended about the time that he got in.

Then he opened up an office at Rockwell and Grand – when he was 26. That was the first office that I can recall because he had a dentist next door to him. It was an all Italian neighborhood. And they were his closest friends. He used to visit with them all the time.

And the amazing thing to me was where he picked up his ethics and talent and drive to go on to become one of the finest surgeons in Chicago. He only wanted to become a surgeon and everyone knew that he was a surgeon's surgeon. If there was a problem requiring a surgeon, my Dad was an expert to fix it.

Then World War II came along. He was on the staff at Norwegian American Hospital from about 1935 to 1971. That's where he died incidentally. There were many Jewish doctors on the staff at NAH at the time. I remember one, Mitchell Nechtow, who was on the staff and who became my Dad's best friend. I would say they were the closest of friends. I know his kids to this day.

Many people called my Dad "Maestro." I don't know if Dad liked that or not but he accepted it. That was his nickname. He was a master surgeon. He was a good father, tough as nails. And he was down to earth in the sense that he was a perfectionist.

I'll tell you how down to earth he was. As a surgeon he never got to see the world as a kid, except that he hitchhiked his way around Lake Michigan after he graduated and was out of high school for a couple of years. Truck drivers would pick him up and buy him lunch. He wanted to see the world and that was his world at the time. He came back afterwards and finished his schooling.

In 1937 when we were kids – there were the two of us – my brother and I – he would load us into the car and every year after that, as long as he could, until he entered the Army in 1942, he would drive us out west or to some state to see the country and we saw almost every state in the Union in a car with no air-conditioning, but he made sure that we had this trip. My brother and I suffered these trips, but Dad would say: "You're going to see this country," which he loved dearly.

While we were in the car, we had to try to memorize the capitals and the major rivers and he would take us to places like Albuquerque, NM and Tucson, AZ in 1938 and there were real Indians there. And I saw Lake Louise in 1939 and Cuba in 1948, since he had a friend there. He took us along. He never had much money, but he made sure that we were included in all of his trips.

The major things that happened in his life at that time involved me and my two brothers, and the Fifth Army, where he spent three and a half years or so overseas before becoming Chief Surgeon with the Fifth Army toward the end of World War II. He became a colonel in the medical corps. He landed with the troops at Anzio and helped set up medical units not only for his own forces, which we called Michael Reese at the time and which became the 16th evacuation unit later on. They needed a surgeon and they needed to form this unit and he volunteered for the job – he didn't have to do this since he was in his 40s. And as a result, he became an absolute expert in surgery of the neck and the hands.

He also helped set up the Brazilian armed forces medical service while serving in Italy and after the war, he was invited by the Brazilian government to visit there and they gave him an honorary medal for service to Brazil and they held a special parade in his honor. That's pretty good for a guy from California and Grand Avenues.

But anyhow a tremendous amount of people respected his ability. He went to Japan; he lectured all over. He worked with the Cook County Hospital Graduate School of Medicine and he was also with the County Hospital as the chief attending surgeon for a while. This was all basically volunteer work. Today everyone gets paid for such efforts and my Dad did a lot of this work, if not totally without pay, it was for very little money. And he loved to teach.

My Dad stuck to his routine at County Hospital and yet made a decent living – a good living, but nothing like doctors make today. But he certainly gave all of us the opportunity to go to college and one of my brothers went to medical school and ended up in the Army and settled in California. I am a University of Illinois graduate and my brother Dick is a Northwestern graduate. I became an agent for New York Life about 40 years ago.

My Dad was extremely loyal to NAH – he really had an affection for that place. He loved their teaching program and that they had nurses that lived there. He felt that the hospital was one of those little jewels of medicine – where you had excellent surgeons and lectures.

The doctors working on staff believed in self-improvement. This was a big thing with him – almost to a fault in his case. He was fantastic in doing the right thing by his patients and medicine.

He wrote a lot. He was an excellent writer. He wrote articles on surgery which were published because he was such an expert – especially on hands and neck. He was really an expert in this area and loved to give clinical demonstrations of his techniques and for that he was clinical professor of surgery at Northwestern for many years. He did many surgeries at Cook County Hospital in the amphitheater and I remember as a kid I used to go to watch him. He hoped perhaps to inspire us to follow in his career.

He was an inspired teacher, but he was a very good father as well. He was tough and he had nothing but his own inspiration to go on.

And he knew a lot of people at Norwegian. They had a lot of interns there at one time from Cuba and those Cubans didn't know where to go on the holidays – Thanksgiving and Christmas. Guess where they ended up – in our house. My Mother and Dad arranged it so that they should not be alone on those holidays. That's an inspired man. I still hear from some of those interns from time to time.

That's why we went to Cuba in '48. We were invited by one doctor's wife, whose husband was called a Commandante in the army at the time. That was when Battista was there and we were there for a week because they wanted to thank him. And of course while he was there he gave a talk at the Cuban Medical School – that's just the kind of person he was.

He died at NAH after a long illness. While he was in the Army he took sick from a rare disease. Picked up a virus which had a long incubation period and caused him to deteriorate mentally about 20 or 30 years after he was discharged. He had his own insurance but NAH kept him as a patient until he died. And this was at a time where there were few nursing homes. He must have been at NAH for five years at least. And my mother visited him every single day.

And my mother was active in the NAH Women's Auxiliary for years and was president of same. With all of this going on, my father was also the President of the Chicago Surgical Society and I remember at one of NAH's functions, there was a Dr. Fauley, I believe, who gave a nice talk about my Dad. It was a nice event and they spoke of my Dad as being the President of the Chicago Surgical Society. His relationship with the hospital was always there. There was no time that I can recall when he was not affiliated in some way with the hospital.

Right after the war, Dad was affiliated with a number of hospitals, but the one he felt closest to was Norwegian. He liked the people and was an integral part of their teaching. As he would put it: "You don't have to be big to be great."

And that just about sums up his philosophy – one that I hope the hospital always follows.

I was flabbergasted with what he was able to do, with what he had. But he still kept a humbleness which was a part of him. Dad's brother also is a doctor – a urologist – and he's still alive and going strong at 91. He's a professor at the University of Illinois.

Dr. Luis Trevino
– Pediatrician on the Medical Staff
of Norwegian American Hospital
for the past 35 years

I started in pediatrics after I finished my training at the University of Illinois and I served full-time at the U of I faculty for several years after the late '50s. I started at NAH in the early '60s so this conversation will reflect the views of the young hispanic (I am a native of Mexico and that is where I did my undergraduate work) coming into an area which was truly a multi-ethnic mix and which was a port of entry of many immigrants including more recently hispanics from Puerto Rico and even earlier people of Italian, Polish or Jewish descent.

It was an interesting mix of ethnic groups in a community that was very vibrant. Norwegian American in the '60s had on their staff many prominent physicians. At that time Cook County Hospital was perhaps the leading institution in the City of Chicago. So I will give you the names of those doctors who were very prominent when I joined the medical staff and who were influential in the leadership of the hospital.

I came in as an associate of a pediatrician by the name of Michael Limosoni, who prior to my association with him had been one of triumvirate of pediatricians who were called the Three L's – Limosani, Lundgoot and Lundberg. And they were the pediatricians not only at NAH but also at Lutheran Deaconess Hospital and St. Elizabeth's and later St. Mary's as well. They had the largest pediatric practice in the area at that time.

At the time there was strong medical leadership exerted by the Jewish doctors – Manuel Lichtenstein, who was a professor of surgery and head of surgery at NAH for many years, and then Mitchell Nechtow, who was the head of obstetrics and a prominent OB-Gyn man at Michael Reese as well.

In orthopedics Dr. Maxwell Corbett, of the Corbett brothers, had an industrial clinic on Lake Street and he was a prominent surgeon. He worked day and night at Norwegian. I remember him making his rounds at midnight and writing his progress notes after seeing a patient. But day after day, he was there.

In the era of the '60s and the early '70s these were the prominent doctors. In education, there were many dedicated individuals. Dr. Murphy, a surgeon who had trained at Mayo Brothers in Rochester and in the latter part of his career was in charge of medical education at NAH, and there was an approved rotating internship in general practice as well.

At the time, the pathologist, Dr. Learner, was very influential as well as the radiologist, Bernard Kleppel, who was very thorough and devoted. Those three come to my mind in education. That does not mean that there were not many others in various specialties who were quite distinguished. There was an orthopedist who is very prominent now – Ahstrom, whose father was here.

But NAH being a community hospital was very strong because it had an excellent staff of family practitioners. In a community of such mixed ethnic background, there had to be some leaders providing healthcare in their respective areas.

There was for example a very strong Italian family practice. There were several doctors who had huge family practices. They were all well trained and were super doctors that did everything, as it was common for family practitioners to do in those days. And foremost in this group was a very prominent man – Dr. Michael Colletti, who was awesome. He delivered babies, he operated, he worked day and night – a very charismatic man and very good with the interns.

Another doctor who was very good and who later developed a ruptured disc that eventually caused him to give up his practice – Dr. Joseph Giosh – both were in their prime. Still another dominant doctor was Dr. Anthony Triolo, very respected and very active in the hospital and on the medical staff. And the fourth of the Italian group that I can recall was Dr. Vince Lombardo, who would stay until 10 or 11 p.m every night. Triolo, Giosh, and Colletti all practiced in the Italian pocket, around Chicago and Grand and Chicago and Western Avenues.

That's not taking anything away from the other general practitioners such as Dr. Victoria Elliot and her husband, Carter Wieneke. And I remember another great family doctor who was I believe Scandinavian – Dr. Anton Jensen, who was a family practitioner of the first order. He did surgery and also delivered babies. He was one that I remember very well because he was older and would make rounds and I remember that the standard of care for a three-pound baby was to take nothing by mouth for 24 hours on the theory that the baby would aspirate and might get pneumonia and choke. And he would come around and argue: "What's the matter with you; why would you starve these babies? They need some nutrition." And in a few years, that nutrition lacking theory went down the tubes and nowadays the first thing they give to these babies is nutrition through IV. So he was proven to be right. This was the pre-neonatology era.

Among the Polish doctors there was Dr. Jan Szewczyk, who was very dynamic. He also did OB, surgery and had a huge practice.

Then in those days there was a significant group of Cuban doctors who were well trained and who had come to the United States at the time that Castro took power in the early '60s. And this was a very welcome addition to the hispanic community which was burgeoning at the time.

In general practice there was Dr. Armando Mendez, who had a huge practice and who was typical. He worked night and day and was an associate of our former medical director, Dr. Pedro Lopez. And there was Dr. Francisco Molina, who was a well known obstetrician on Clark Street who practiced here for a long time. His associate was a doctor who was first class, Dr. Serafin Dominguez, who died young.

There were still other Cubans who were prominent on the staff. One was the anesthesiologist, Dr. Pablo Zalduendo, who was in charge of anesthesia for a long time and later brought in his brother who was also an anesthesiologist and they took care of most of the surgery. Just the two of them and a few nurses, which was very impressive. Another was a urologist, Dr. Alfonso Diaz, who seemed to be the head of urology forever, and Dr. Gabriel Rodriguez, who was the head of obstetrics and then brought in another Cuban, Dr. Rafael Ortiz, who had trained at the University of Chicago, and who was very dynamic and charismatic. There were also general practitioners such as Dr. Ignacio Fornaris.

I also recall a Spaniard, who was a colleague of mine in the same office building as me, Dr. Esteban Ortiz, who came from Spain and who was here at NAH at least 20 years, and two fine doctors from the Dominican Republic who were very prominent in the community – one was Dr. Luis Diaz-Perez, who had been president of the medical staff, and the other was Dr. Ramon Garcia Camilo, who had a huge practice at the intersection of Ashland, Madison and Ogden and who later became an allergist, with additional training.

There was also Dr. Enrique Lipezker, an Argentinian, and Dr. Edmundo Rioja from Bolivia and Dr. Eduardo Barriuso, who was also very strong in obstetrics, who came from Bolivia. They were the pillars in the building of the perinatal center at NAH. And I certainly don't want to omit my fellow countryman and a pillar of our OB-Gyne Department, Dr. Procopio Munoz, who is still very active today.

Certainly one of the things that turned the hospital around was the administration idea to proceed to modernize the maternity facilities, and that turned out very well because the facilities for obstetrics and delivery helped put Norwegian in the top ten in maternities in the state.

I have omitted one of the most charismatic and great doctors on our staff, Dr. John Cavenagh, who was in practice at Norwegian for decades in the area of cardiology. From the Philippines we had Drs. Botuyan, Ladlad, DeLeon and Munez, who was an associate of mine.

I remember a Dr. Paneque, who was with Dr. Colletti, and his son got sick when the kid was 6 or 7 years old and it looked like he had rheumatic heart disease. I told him I would ask my professor, who was in cardiology at the University of Illinois and later head of pediatrics at Cook County, to examine the child. It turned out that he did have rheumatic heart disease and this doctor told me that his father had had a practice at the corner of North Avenue and California for many years. At the time he used to come to Norwegian, and it was a pleasure for me to make this visit, he told me.

But the hospital is still vibrant through the leadership of our Board chairman, Mr. Dahl, and the new group of doctors who are leading the hospital today. One of our prize interns during my time was Dr. Villalba who was a bright intern when the rotating internship was in force. He and Dr. Dumpit and Dr. Munez were interns when I was attending and they all received tremendous training here and came back as specialists. Dr. Villalba as a urologist and Dr. Dumpit in family practice and Dr. Munez in pediatrics.

**Dr. Pedro Lopez
– Retired, former Director of
Continuing Medical Education and
Medical Director/V.P., Medical Affairs**

As Director of Continuing Medical Education until my recent retirement, my job was to present all teaching programs to the medical staff from the time of my appointment to this position in 1977. Later, I was Medical Director, in charge of relations with the medical staff, from 1991 until my retirement.

I received my medical training at the University of Havana in Cuba in 1955 followed by an internship and residency there from 1956 to 1957. I then came directly to St. Anne's Hospital in Chicago for additional residency training for two and a half years in family practice. Finally, I came to Norwegian American Hospital in 1961.

I knew several of the doctors when I came here and it was natural to associate with them. I first got acquainted with the hospital through my association with Dr. Valdez and Dr. Ramon Mendez, who was an associate of his.

So when I became Director of Continuing Education in 1977, I had been associated with NAH for 16 years. And I was practicing until I became full-time medical director at the hospital in 1991.

Over the years I have seen a tremendous amount of changes both in building and in the number of beds. This would include the renovation in our obstetrics department and in the pediatric floor and of course the new surgical suite.

In addition, the hospital has become, over the years, the primary hospital for community residents of Latino background, for several reasons. Number one is the location, in the heart of the Latino community, and secondly for the large number of Spanish-speaking physicians on the staff and last, but not least, for the fine quality of care available to the community at this hospital.

For the future, we must continue to move ahead and keep abreast of the changes, not only in the delivery of health care but also in the new financial payment and delivery systems – the trend toward managed care.

As to managed care, the hospital has done about as well as it could, given the circumstances surrounding reimbursement for services. Under managed care, this has been a problem for all healthcare providers.

Over the years I have been associated with many fine and outstanding physicians at NAH. In the early years, I was close to Dr. Lichtenstein and Dr. Nechtow. I developed a strong friendship with both of them as well as Dr. Isoe, who took care of many of my surgical patients. They were not only good doctors, but they were good people – gentlemen. In the years since, I have been in contact with the total medical staff, but in particular, I would mention Dr. Campanini, in the laboratory, who has done a superb job, and Dr. Lopata in X-ray who came here from Walther Memorial after they closed.

As to the rest of the doctors that I have known and admired, I would probably have to list the entire medical staff.

Over the years, the medical staff here has been in a position to provide good, sound medical care. The names may have changed, but others have picked up the slack and carried on as good or better as was true of bygone days.

It should be noted that not only has Norwegian American helped to upgrade the quality of medical care in this community, but through its various policies, it has helped to clean up the area to make it look more attractive and to provide better security, and has served to work with the people in the community for various events including free health screenings and instruction in such things as lessons for new fathers and mothers on the care of their newborns.

Perhaps the main benefit the hospital has offered the community is that all residents can receive service whenever needed regardless of their socioeconomic status.

I might point out that the relationship between the medical staff, the Board and administration has been excellent in recent years. It is much better today thanks to our former Board chairman, Norman Dahl, who has seen to it that the Staff has greater input on the operations of the hospital through the Board and as a result, we are much closer in working together as members of the same team.

I am a prime example of how administration and staff are working closer together. I was given an administrative post as Medical Director to help to improve relations between both administration and the staff and the board.

I can only add that I am confident that we will be here no matter what happens in the future. Of course much will depend on the policies that the state works out for reimbursement under Medicaid, but I am optimistic. I believe that it won't be too long before we see a reversal of some of the restrictive policies on reimbursement which have had such a negative effect on hospitals in this area and in the area of managed care. Under the latter, the HMOs have been managing their businesses very well, but they don't do much for the patients.

Dr. Eduardo Ladlad
– Former president of the medical staff,
founding president of the Norwegian American
Hospital Century Lions Club and a prime participant
of the Medical Missions to foreign lands

I am in private practice and specialize in OB-Gyn. I have been associated with this hospital for more than 25 years. Originally, I was an intern at Norwegian in 1968 and then I did one year of general surgery in 1969 and I completed my residency at Cook County Hospital for four years in OB-Gyn. I've been here ever since.

Through my internship at NAH, I decided to come to Norwegian, because I knew many of the attending physicians associated with the hospital at the time. I have been involved in several projects connected with the hospital and the medical staff in recent years including the organization and the steering committee of the Century PHO, a physicians and hospital agency which contracts with HMOs to provide various medical and hospital services.

I was also the charter president of the Norwegian American Century Lions Club, which was chartered in connection with the hospital Centennial in 1993-94. I have been associated with the Lions since I was a young lad back in my home country – in the Philippines. And I was recruited by various Lions Clubs in the years since. In connection with organizing the Lions Club at the hospital – the Century Lions Club – I asked how many members are required in order to charter a new club and the answer was 20. Well, I thought to myself, I can do better than that. With the help of friends and of course, Mr. Dahl, I was able to get 100 members willing to join as charter members of the Lions Club.

Our first project was undertaking the missions to foreign lands. There had been other medical missions abroad for many years through the Philippine Medical Society and the Illinois Philippine Medical Society – so this goes back about 15 or 20 years ago. Even when I was a student, there were missions to rural areas in the Philippines, so I was familiar with this program.

So in 1993, during our very first meetings, we were talking about various projects that we could undertake, and there was talk of doing 100 projects for the hospital from various groups during the Centennial year. One of the suggestions was to do medical missions. This was made possible through the cooperation of the Lions Club. There have been 16 missions in all to date, including six to the Philippines and others to other countries.

I personally have been involved in organizing these missions and in the fundraising every year. But I was a participant on the missions for the first three years. For the past few years, however, because of other commitments, I have not been able to be involved in the Missions to the Philippines.

There are many benefits to all involved in these medical missions overseas. For the physician, it is a personal sense of gratification that they have helped those less fortunate. Perhaps we are only able to see a few hundred patients or so on one mission, but for those patients seen during the Mission with those problems in my specialty, tumors of the uterus and ovaries, the missions have meant the difference between life or death – before, they might have had this for years and they would die with these tumors. Now they have an opportunity to have it taken care of 100 percent. This may be scratching the surface of the overall needs of the people, but for the one that is helped to better health and to a possible avoidance of what might have been a certain death, it is wonderful. They are able to continue to work throughout their lifetime. During a typical mission, we might perform a few hundred surgeries and see several thousand outpatients in all.

Generally speaking, the missions are aimed at the indigent or poor people – those who cannot afford their own health care. It might be those with cleft palate, cleft lip or tumors.

The other side effect of this mission is the goodwill that we bring to the people of the countries that we visit – from the United States and from Chicago.

To my knowledge Norwegian American is unique in undertaking all of these medical missions to foreign lands. I don't know of any other hospitals that are doing this. There are medical groups that do this such as those that I mentioned before, the Philippine Medical Association and the Illinois Philippine Medical Society, but no other hospitals per se that do this.

I have also been active in the formation of a medical staff investment club. This came about because physicians are very poor investors and often put their money in the bank where they earn very little interest. So one day we talked about how to improve our insurance plans, and our profit sharing, and I said, why don't we organize a club where we can talk about these things on a monthly basis and have a speaker. That's how we organized the club. We have 39 members and this has been going on now for five years. Now the members are more interested in exploring the stock market and investments.

As to the golf association, that began because the hospital is composed of several ethnic groups – physicians from various countries, including India, China, Korea, the Philippines – so we got the idea of trying to get these various doctors together in one common group. In that respect this hospital is truly unique in that the doctors are together now. Golf is one game that all physicians can play. It is not too strenuous, like tennis, for instance. So we organized the Golf Association to help keep us close-knit and now we have 45 members, all physicians, who are interested in playing golf. We go out together. We go out of state once a year and that helps to keep us close.

In the 25 years that I have been associated with Norwegian American, there has been a tremendous amount of internal revamping and renovations of departments. But externally, there has been a complete renovation of the area too – as we have acquired and torn down various dilapidated buildings and replaced them with landscaping and good lighting which makes for much better security. Only 15 years ago, many were afraid to come to this hospital. Now they see the attractive landscaping and how bright it is, even at night, and of course the Professional Building is only a few years old and gives the hospital a whole new image.

Inside, every department has been expanded and renovated. ICU has been expanded and the Emergency Room is now comprehensive and is five times bigger than before and takes all kinds of ambulance patients. Before it was unable to do this. The Operating Room is an entirely new unit built out from the center of the hospital. It's an all new facility with all new equipment.

The delivery room is now good for patients who can stay in the same room for labor, delivery and recovery. What's more, we have installed private rooms for all patients who have delivered their babies and the mothers and their babies now stay in the same room. I am very much involved as senior attending physician in OB-Gyn.

I believe that in the future the hospital will continue as the primary Latino hospital in this area. The outpatients are now more comfortable coming here.

There will be affiliation with other institutions, such as the recently signed agreement with Illinois Masonic for services not now available at this hospital, and contracts with HMOs as a backdrop for certain neurosurgical services and ancillary care services.

I have remained with Norwegian for all of these years because among others this hospital provides the finest OB service. Other hospitals are starting to become involved in this area but many have not given this priority. Norwegian has always been very strong in this department. We were the first to have a neonatologist to care for newborns who require attention, and the first to have a perinatologist to care for mothers who might require special attention before their deliveries.

The Family Practice residency program, I believe, is the next step for the hospital. Our doctors, including myself, are getting older, and so are our patients. Pretty soon these doctors will be retiring. To replace them, it's getting harder and harder to recruit. Now if we had a residency program, which we are in the process of starting, that would serve as the future of the hospital. Residents who complete the program here would tend to stay here because they are familiar with the hospital – they know everybody and in addition the hospital usually sets up their practice while they train here so they stay on with their practice already built in during their training.

Debbie Borucki
– Former Vice President of Patient Care Services

I received my bachelors degree in nursing from the University of Illinois in '93 and have a masters degree in business management, which I received in '96.

I originally received my associates degree in nursing from Triton College in '84 and started part-time at Norwegian that same year. Later I went back to school and got my bachelors degree and in '91, I became nurse manager of the special care (infant's) nursery.

In '93 I became director of nursing and in '98 I was promoted to Vice President of Patient Care Services. My responsibilities were much broader. I had nursing, TQI (Total Quality Improvement) and UR (utilization review).

But nursing was about the largest of patient care services, which totaled nearly 300 employees, including about 190 RN's.

We asked that all of our nurses be certified in their various specialties by the American Nursing Association by the year 2000. Currently about 35 percent of our nurses are certified by specialty.

It involves intensive study in their specialty and then they have to pass the boards for their specialty. In order to take the test, you had to have at least two years' experience in your specialty and each area has its own standards which you must complete before you are allowed to take the test. So, all of our RN's will be credentialed in their various specialties by the year 2000.

For example, I am credentialed in nursing administration and in order to qualify, I had to have so many years of experience and so many hours of continuing education to take the board for nursing administration. And then you had to pass the board and that is no snap. Some passed their specialty board with no trouble and others had to take it two or three times to pass.

Take our Emergency Room nurses, for example. They had to have at least two to three years of experience in the Emergency Room and 100 hours of continuing education before they were allowed to sit for their boards.

Our purpose in making credentialing in the various specialties a requirement was to make sure that our nurses were competent in their specialties and this was one way of assuring this. This is very important because the patients entering the hospital today are sicker than was the case before and our nurses had to have more skills and education to handle their needs.

When I was here, I saw a lot of growth. We increased our staffing considerably, but probably the most significant change occurred in our Obstetrics services since 1994. 1994 is when we brought in a neonatologist and in-house pediatricians around the clock because our OB service was so busy and high risk. We had in-house neonatology during the day and they worked strictly with newborns but we also had board certified pediatricians working around the clock.

About two years ago we hired a perinatologist – a physician that specializes in maternal medicine. They have even more training than an obstetrician. Very few hospitals have perinatologists. We were one of the few community hospitals that had one. If an obstetrician has an extremely high risk delivery, they will call in the perinatologist for consultation and they usually will take over the care of the patient until they deliver the baby.

All of our nurses in OB were neonatal certified in resuscitation. This is required of all nurses involved in the labor and delivery rooms. It's called NALS, and it stands for Neonatal Advanced Life Support.

We were anticipating a shortage of skilled nurses in the near future and put together a strategic plan to bring in some nurses. We were actively recruiting schools of nursing to do their clinical rotations at Norwegian because this is a good way to bring nurses into the hospital.

We were also developing an internship and scholarship program for nurses to come to work here, but offered an internship for nursing students during their senior year. We met with the deans of the various schools in an effort to get this launched.

Our nurse turnover was very low. Most of the nurses had been here for at least ten years or more and I attribute this to the very warm, family atmosphere that we had at Norwegian. Our pay scale was good but probably no higher than any other community hospital for comparable nurses. But the thing that stands out most is that we provided 100 percent tuition reimbursement to our staff and that attracted a lot of staff.

We also paid for any costs involved by our nurses in obtaining their certification for their specialty. We had a good educational and financial reimbursement plan.

And we recognized our nurses' educational achievements. Say for instance a nurse received her bachelors degree in nursing. They got a 2 percent increase in salary immediately and if they became certified in their areas of specialty, they got another two percent increase in pay. If they went for their masters, they got another 2 percent increase.

As to the negative things that you hear about nursing, I think that is greatly exaggerated. One of the things that has happened is that new nurses would join our staff and they had a different vision of what nurses do – a sort of glorified version of nursing. That they would not, for instance, have to do bedpans and that was not true at all of our nursing staff at Norwegian, where we provided total nursing care for our patients – where they had to hold the hands of the patients and had to be there all of the time. Some of the younger nurses found this disturbing because it's not necessarily what they had been led to believe they will be doing in school.

We had primary nursing in the ICU and in the nursery and in the labor and delivery which meant that all of our nursing staff had total care of patients – we didn't have nursing assistants – they were all nurses.

During the past year one of our major achievements was to receive pediatric certification in the Emergency Room from the Illinois Department of Public Health.

In the past year, we converted our post delivery areas to mother-baby private rooms so that the Mom has a private room and the baby can stay with her 24 hours a day along with the husband, who may stay overnight. Before we had double rooms and we couldn't do this. We had 16 private rooms and another unit with double rooms for mothers who had not delivered their babies.

But we avoided filling these up with two people unless we had to. And we had renovated our post-delivery area with new draperies and equipment to make it look nicer and homier.

Also, we started our Women's Center about a year and a half ago and offered various services for women of all ages – there were teen services, mid-life services, prenatal services and so forth. We were very busy in that Center and as a result increased our admissions not only in OB but in medical and surgical. Our midlife services for women who were going through menopause or any other problems. We offered them mammograms and all of the other services they required to maintain their health.

We offered one-day services – so that they received all of the tests and were seen by a physician. They also could get a massage and we had a social worker available for their needs.

So, what it amounts to is that our OB numbers were down slightly, but our medical, surgical and ICU greatly increased, which is why we were in the process of building a new ICU, which is state-of-the-art. It has gone from eight to 12 beds, and opened in July.

Our present ICU is usually full. We were always running out of beds and this was true of telemetry, which was also rapidly expanding. We had a 21 bed telemetry unit and a three bed dialysis unit and that proved very helpful.

Ellen Pedersen
– Widow of Marshall Pedersen, long-time member
of the Norwegian American Hospital Board, and
mother of Dr. Marshall Pedersen

I was active in the Women's Auxiliary. At the time there were many doctors' wives and others on the Board of the Auxiliary, from about 1967 through 1972. My husband Marshall was on the Board for many years and before that his father, John Pedersen, was on the Board when the hospital was founded in 1894.

We always had bazaars, sales, once a year and we also would hold rummage sales. We were always holding special sales to raise money. Heidi, or as we called her, Honey Warden, was a stimulator and she was the one that got the gift shop and the Auxiliary as well going. All of the doctors' wives automatically became members and so was I because my husband, Marshall Senior, was on the Board of Trustees.

The ladies always had a dinner dance, which they had held for years. It was already going when I became a member and Honey Warden was the one that got that started. These were always held in the top hotels in Chicago and then we had our style shows. They were fabulous and we had several at the Drake. That was the hotel that we used for the style show when I was on the Board. I remember that these style shows used to be fabulously attended. My sister Arlene graduated from the school of nursing. She was Arlene Gullicksen.

Arlene Gullicksen
– Sister of Ellen Pedersen, widow of Marshall Pedersen, Sr. –
and a graduate of the NAH School of Nursing

I graduated from the school of nursing in 1952. My late brother-in-law, Marshall Pedersen, knew I was going to nursing school and he told me: "If you don't go into training at NAH, I'll never speak to you again."

Indirectly, through a doctor there, I met my future husband, who was born there, and my two children were born there.

After I finished my training, I worked in the hospital for about a year and a half or two. It was in 1955 that I married Mr. Gullicksen.

I had a very nice class and had been in the business world for a while, so I was several years older than most of the other students in nursing school. It took me a while to blend in with them. It was a three-year program and we had no summers off. My daughter went to the University of Iowa and became a nurse also and she had summers off. We only got two weeks off a year.

We had classes in the day and in the evening and if we worked the morning, we would also have classes for several hours. I was fortunate in that I knew shorthand, so when we would have doctors' lectures, I could take notes. I was also a typist and could type my study cases.

We had about 16 in the class. We had to be in by 10 p.m. and we lived in the hospital. I remember that when I was in the delivery room, my sister, Ellen, had both of her children delivered there. The delivery room, I believe, was on the fifth floor and the nursery on the fourth floor and after the children were delivered and identified we had to take them to the nursery, so I gave my niece Anita, her first ride. Now the delivery rooms and the nursery are all on one floor.

I remember Dr. Sidney Brown and Dr. Isoe, he was a surgeon. Dr. Brown was a GP.

I worked in the delivery room when I finished school. I live in Park Ridge and I still work at St. Matthew Home and I take blood pressures in a bank and I do some work for Wellness, Inc., which gives flu shots and blood tests.

My husband was on the Board for a while. Then he became too busy with his own business – the Hammond Organ Co.

I remember that there were two Nelson sisters in my class. They were from Daggett, Michigan, and there were four or five of them that graduated from NAH.

Elysene Corder
– Sister-in-law of Ellen Pedersen

I remember that Signe Reid was the daughter of Mr. Krabol, who was the Chairman of the Board during the '20s and the '30s, and Elmer Abrahamson was the lawyer for many years. He died a few years ago and his second wife is still living.

We gave style shows and luncheons and we would have several hundred in attendance. My brother, Marshall Pedersen Sr., was on the Board for many years and so was my father. The style shows were how we made our money.

I remember that when my husband was in the hospital for two weeks, the whole bill was $60. That was in 1934 or 1935. We live in Stoughton, Wisconsin, which is populated primarily by people of Norwegian descent. We have a nursing home which is probably one of the finest in the state. It has 268 patients and next to it is a little hospital and we have the largest 17th of May celebration in the United States and many people come to our home town to see it.

Many girls from our town went to nursing school at NAH but it got so expensive that they did away with that. That's when the nurses wore stiff skirts and aprons.

William Korsvik
– Retired member of the Board of Trustees

I was on the Board at NAH from about 1965 to 1980 and served as treasurer for part of that time. I'm a retired banker. My uncle was Birger Osland, who was Board Chairman of NAH during the Depression, and who married my father's sister.

The hospital was having financial difficulties at the time. It was during the heart of the Depression, which was much before my time. My impression of what happened was that the hospital could not pay its debts, but largely through the efforts of my uncle, the hospital was able to persuade their creditors to take long-term bonds, or debentures, and the First National Bank of Chicago was the trustee for these bonds.

I'm sure that by today's standards the debt was relatively small, but for those days, it was a lot. And through this bond issue they were tided over until they were able to obtain the funds to pay off the bonds, and the creditors who held these bonds agreed to hold off payment on same for several years. By the early '40s, the hospital was in pretty good shape and clear of debt. They liquidated the debt, paid off the bank, which in turn paid off the bondholders.

What was interesting was that the hospital was this close to folding at the time, but was able to surmount this problem and this reflects the financial leadership that Birger Osland was able to bring to the hospital.

As an investment banker, he had an excellent reputation and was able to obtain the support of the First National Bank as a result.

He established his investment company in the mid-'20s selling bonds primarily. He's been dead about 30 years now.

During my tenure on the Board, there was some discussion about members of the Board profiting from hospital contracts or services – such as architectural or contractual services in building construction projects. This was disturbing to some of us because of the possibility of conflict of interest. In a sense some members of the Board were involved in letting contracts to themselves and partially as a result of this discussion, the hospital severed its relations with the First National Bank, since I was associated with the bank at the time. While the amount of money on deposit at the bank was insignificant, we transferred the account to another bank to avoid the appearance of impropriety.

I was connected with the First National Bank for many years and when I left, I was senior vice president. I retired from the bank in '82 and I had already left the NAH Board at that time. While I was with the hospital, I felt that I had information and access to material that was of value in the hospital's operations and so when I was leaving, I severed my connection with the hospital and various other boards that I was connected with, including the Norwegian American Hospital Foundation.

In my experience with NAH, the two outstanding leaders were Norm Dahl and Birger Osland.

Of course I saw quite a change in the patient population and the medical staff which was changing even then. There was some discussion about whether we should abandon the area and move elsewhere, but thanks to Norm we decided to stay in the late '70s.

As to the future, it will depend to a great extent on how generous the state will be in its support of Medicaid patients, which make up a large share of the hospital's patients. Also the role of medicine has changed quite a bit. My daughter is a physician and not too long ago she said that if she had it to do over again, she would not have gone into medicine because of all of the restrictions and restraints which prevent doctors from doing the things that they feel are necessary to practice quality medicine.

Also, in my time at the hospital, the medical staff was not as much a part of the Board as it is today. In fact one of the big debates was whether or not we should admit any doctors to the Board and this took place about the time I was leaving. There was some doubt as to whether the Board discussions should be open to the medical staff. Eventually Dr. Larsandrew Dolan was the first physician admitted to the Board. Today we have several doctors on the Board and as a result, the degree of cooperation between the Board and the medical staff is phenomenal, which was not the case before.

One of the first efforts to raise money and to develop an esprit de corps between the various hospital groups was the result of Art Bagge, who started the annual fundraiser and ball, the Viking Ball, held in the Fall. Art was the one who spearheaded this effort which was a success from the very start in 1963. And it was Art who was personally responsible in large part to the success which this annual affair has enjoyed over the years.

When it first started out the Ball earned about $10,000 or so per year. Today it clears several hundred thousand each year. I still maintain touch with the hospital through Norm Dahl and Art Bagge, since we are all part of the Norwegian American Pioneers, a Norwegian social organization.

Art Bagge
– Long-time member of the Board of
Trustees Now Retired

My years with the Board go back to '63. In 1963, the Chairman of the Board was John Hanson, who happened to be our family lawyer for many years. One day out of the blue, he walked into my office in the Prudential Building and asked me if I would like to be on the Board. I told him frankly that I did not know anything about hospital work, but if he thought I could contribute, I would be happy to do so.

From the time I graduated from Northwestern University in 1931, I've been in advertising sales. My first job was with the Dictaphone Company right out of school and I went to Bridgeport, CT and went to their factory and learned how to make a dictaphone. Then I was on their sales force in Chicago.

Then I was with A.C. Nielsen Co., here in Chicago and was one of the first members of the Nielsen organization to conduct their survey on food and drug stores throughout the country to see how their products were moving to the consumer, so I traveled at that time from coast to coast. Eventually, I was promoted to head of chain stores, so I would go to the headquarters of the big chains such as Walgreen's and Osco and all of those people.

Then I transferred to Nielsen's offices on Fifth Avenue in New York, where I was assistant to Mr. Nielsen and then I became an account man for Gillette and other products.

Subsequently, I joined the William Randolph Hearst organization and was the youngest salesman they ever hired to sell space in the American Weekly, which was the publication distributed with all the Sunday Hearst papers. I was with them for 19 years, selling national advertising. After that, I went into the radio and TV business and was a station representative. I represented about 33 radio stations and 30 TV stations all over the country and sold all of their national advertising for them. When I retired from this position, that was it.

I was on the Board for 33 years. I ran the Viking Ball for 17 years, from about 1963 until 1980 or so. We always made money, about $15,000 to $18,000 per year. That was a lot of money at the time. Today they make a couple of hundred thousand dollars, in part because they have all kinds of ad books and so forth, which they did not have then.

We had quite a few Norwegians on the Board when I started, and today we have only three or four. There were also a number of Norwegian doctors on the staff and today we have none. So the fact that we are called Norwegian American Hospital is just a title, which does not reflect what the hospital is today. But just as it was at the time that I started, we still serve a very important place in the community.

At first the hospital was a part of the Lutheran Church in 1885 when the first meeting of the Norwegian Lutheran Tabitha Society was held. Then in 1889, the Board at that time decided to find a site for the new building, which they purchased for $5,000 and the cornerstone was laid in 1894. The first patient was admitted in December 1894.

In 1902 we were using adjacent apartment buildings for a nurses' residence and three years later built a building for the nurses to live in. And in 1910 the hospital became non-sectarian and went off from the Lutheran mission. In 1917 they built a new Nurses' Home.

In the years since, the hospital has simply mushroomed and the Professional Building is brand new, all paid for and completely booked. It cost $11 million to put up. During my years on the Board, I was on the Strategic Planning Committee, on the Governance Committee, the Nominating Committee, the Executive Committee, the Compensation Committee, the Viking Ball Committee, of course, and the Selection Committee.

There were times when I was at the hospital three to four times a week; now, I recently retired.

There were some very serious problems during my 35 year tenure on the Board and even before then. For example, right after the Depression the hospital was broke and went into voluntary bankruptcy for about a half million dollars. But thanks to Birger Osland, who provided the leadership that we needed, we survived.

Then about 20 years ago some of the doctors wanted to buy the hospital and to change the name to the Spanish American Hospital and to make it a for profit hospital, but we voted that down quick. About 27 years ago we had a serious labor strike. The Unions would not allow us to take things in or out of the hospital – not even the garbage.

The Trustees and the doctors had to bring in milk in their brief cases. While this might have been considered a rough neighborhood at the time, this worked to our advantage during the strike. Because while the strike was going on, the father of one of the leading gangs in the area heard about the strike and he told his son about it. Before we knew what had happened, the Latin Kings told the Union to get out of our hospital, or they would be sorry.

About 15 years ago we thought we were going to be wonderful and put in a fancy computer system for the nurses' station for billing – we tried it out for a couple of years and we lost our shirts on it.

Then in the early '80s we contracted with National Medical Enterprises to run the hospital. They did a good job, but it was very costly. Norman Dahl said, "Hey, we can do as good as they can," and we terminated their contract.

Yes, I have roots in this community although I live in the North Suburbs now. My father came from Norway in 1899 and where did he settle – on California and North Avenues and for years, I would march in the big Norwegian parade at California and North on the 17th of May, when I was a boy, and today, they have this parade in Park Ridge.

He brought with him professional racing skates given to him by a world champion who was Norwegian – they were 19 inches long and the steel was so hard, that he took those skates to race with and the police chased him off the ice because he was going too fast. Then the Johnson Skate people modeled their skates after those that my Dad brought with him and they are at the Museum in Decorah, Iowa.

Right now, we serve a very positive function in this community and the Latino people in the area consider this as their hospital and they depend on it. But we in turn have to depend on Springfield to help pay for the 55 percent or so who are on public aid, and we have to survive on that. If they should somehow not decide to help the inner city hospitals, it would cut off a lot of our income. But with a good Board and good management, we are surviving and even moving ahead.

Bob Baker
– Retired consultant in public relations and former member of the Board of Trustees

I came to NAH in 1968 and have been affiliated with the hospital in various capacities almost 31 years. I started as a consultant in public relations and have my own business – the Ealy-Baker Organization that later became Baker-Bowden, Inc. We were a PR agency, but I sold the business in 1980 and hired a young lady, Marcy Whitney Schenck, to act as PR director in 1990. When I resigned the account, I became a member of the Board a year later.

When I started in '68, the hospital was going along on a pretty profitable keel, but under a previous administrator, we started to encounter problems in the early '70s and started to show a decline in admissions and profitability, and this became critical, so the hospital Board began to search for a new administrator, but to no avail, so they wound up by contracting with an outside firm – National Medical Enterprises – to provide the Administrator and that's when we brought in Bill Leyhe. There were some rough moments to begin with, but then we started climbing again. Leyhe did a great job.

From that point on it's been a slow trend upward with some dips but miraculously the hospital has survived. And since then we have dedicated the new Professional Building last year, after years of debate about whether or not we should build it and where it should be located. For a while, it was suggested that we locate the new building on the west side of the hospital, but that would have involved the demolition of a church as well as a few other buildings, so we went ahead and built it directly east of the hospital.

And of course, when I came to NAH, the Norwegian influence was already fading and the Hispanic doctors were beginning to come in. Now the mix is very heavy in Filipino and Hispanic doctors primarily, who have trained overseas.

In the early years, the hospital had 265 beds, but today the times are entirely different and our daily census is less than a hundred patients most of the time, and by all odds we should be in deep trouble, but we continue to make money and I am amazed that we are able to do so.

There were of course many staff members that stand out, but to my way of thinking, Dr. Lichtenstein was outstanding. He was still active in '68 until the early 70's, but he was quite a phenomenal guy. He was a specialist in neck and hand surgery. There were several others who were quite good, including Dr. Isadore Isoe and Dr. Larsandrew Dolan and Dr. Cavenagh, an excellent heart specialist, and Dr. Trevino was a top physician in pediatrics.

But the number of hospitals is dwindling and has gone from about 14,000 to less than half that number today, which makes our achievements in operating this hospital and still showing a profit all the more outstanding.

As to the future, the hospital will continue to be a major force in healthcare in this community as long as it is able to survive.

Then of course there was the effort to unionize the hospital in 1972, and it was a major problem to get milk into the hospital. I remember that my wife and I would make frequent trips to the hospital and would be carrying milk to the hospital. That was certainly a part of the hospital history and something that I can never forget.

Chris Johansen – Retired Vice Chairman of the Board of Trustees and Former Member of the Board of Trustees

When I first joined the Board, more than 40 years ago, I knew two people on the Board – Marshall Pedersen, son of John Pedersen, owner of a local mortuary, and Dr. Rasmus Harr, a member of our medical staff.

I grew up in Humboldt Park and used to play baseball in the park when I was about ten years old. We lived just a little south of North Avenue on Whipple Street, but I used to come out in the summertime when it was about 90 degrees and my brother and I would sleep out in the park.

I am a graduate of Lane Tech, class of 1940. When I went there it was 100 percent boys. But I was familiar with the hospital long before I joined the Board, having had my tonsils removed at NAH when I was a lad.

When I joined the Board I was an engineer with Zenith Radio Corporation and after a long period of service there, I retired in 1986 after 20 years of service at Zenith.

Since joining the Board, I've witnessed many achievements over the years, but in my mind our number one accomplishment is that we cleaned up the area. There was a time about 30 years ago or so when you wouldn't dare to walk around Humboldt Park or in this area without being afraid of being mugged or assaulted. There is none of that now. We tore down a lot of the old houses and put in parking areas all around the hospital and we have security all around the hospital perimeter.

There were not too many doctors of Norwegian ancestry on our medical staff when I joined the Board. Many were leaving or had already left the hospital and the Hispanic doctors were coming in.

Probably our greatest problem that we overcame were the financial difficulties that we encountered around the '80s. The census was down and our finances were down and that's when we contracted with National Medical Enterprises to tap their experience and knowhow in running the hospital and they sent us Bill Leyhe to head our management. That helped a lot, but the real credit has to go to our doctors who have responded to our efforts to have them bring their patients here. And today our doctors love the hospital, as all of us on the Board do. It's a very clean hospital. And you don't have any gangs here, such as there were when I first joined the Board.

We draw patients from the entire northwest side of Chicago and from the west side and the near south side as well. So our patient population is by and large Hispanic.

My particular assignment on the Board was to work with the Campus Beautification Committee. I helped to buy the various buildings and houses and then to have them torn down to build some of the additions that we have made over the years including parking and if you notice now, we have parking surrounding the entire building. It's all so much brighter – and that has been a godsend for this hospital. There was a time when people did not want to come here – especially at night. Not any more. Now they come day or night. And our security completely surrounds the hospital and guards the hospital very well.

Our main strength has been that we offer the best in nursery and maternity facilities for mothers to be. We have been and still are one of the biggest as far as the number of babies delivered per year – we have had as many as 4,000 babies in one year, which puts us in the top bracket in the state for the number of babies born in one year.

Along with the many babies that are born here, we admit a large number of children every year for various diseases and illnesses, primarily in the area of respiratory conditions.

One of the things that has been very attractive for our medical staff and the patients is the fact that we are known for serving some of the best food of any hospital in Chicago. Many doctors come here just for the food and we have doctors coming from the entire area. We have approximately four doctors on the Board right now and several who are serving emeritus who do not have a vote.

One thing about our Norwegian heritage is our conservatism as far as finances are concerned. We tend not to overreach our resources. The new Professional Building for instance – which was put up at a cost of $11 million – was completely paid for out of our own funds. We didn't have to borrow a penny.

The main expansion that we have had in recent years was the completion of the new wing in the late '50s which gave us additional beds and facilities for our nursing school. But since then there has been considerable remodeling and revamping of our departments, including our pediatrics unit, our nursery, our OB and delivery rooms, and our new surgical wing – which opened a few years ago. And our new emergency room was completely revamped and expanded.

As to the future, we have been doing so well in recent years that I don't see any reason why we should change as long as we are alert to the needs of the community and can offer these services as they develop. We're one of the few hospitals in the Chicago area and for that matter in the entire nation that is in the black. So I am proud of this hospital. And we are getting more Medicare patients (those over 65 who are on Social Security) and that's a good thing for the hospital.

One of the toughest problems we have had to overcome is the greed of property owners who make it tough to acquire property in the area surrounding the hospital.

For example, just east of the hospital, where we have one of our parking lots, was a big U – shaped apartment building. I believe it was about 40 apartments in all. We wanted to buy this property and the fellow that owned it wanted $44,000 or so and we decided to buy it. So when we came back to offer him the price that he said that he wanted, he changed his mind and told us that he now wanted $100,000. By the time that we got back to buying the building he wanted $160,000, and that's what we had to pay.

Another example, there's a tumble down shack of a building, just south of the doctors' parking lot – probably not worth more than $15,000, perhaps $20,000, but the owner wanted more and we offered him up to $100,000 and he turned us down. He wanted $160,000, which was too high for us, so we turned him down. And now he sits with that building and we built a parking lot around it.

One of the most satisfying things we do at NAH is to offer scholarships – we take two students from Norway and bring them here for study. They are college students who want to enter the health professions. And we have the Foundation, which awards 10 to 15 scholarships a year to area high school students who want to enter the health professions.

We're also working on setting up a fitness program with exercise equipment in the basement which should be operational soon. And I might mention that Sammy Sosa's wife had her baby here four or five months ago – which is a testimonial of the hospital's reputation.

In 1975 we had a visit from King Olav, who visited the hospital, and then his son, King Harald V was here in connection with the Centennial and the groundbreaking of the new Professional Building in 1995.

Then of course, we have each year since the Centennial in 1993-94 sponsored missions to medically underserved countries in Latin America and in the Philippines. This has brought medical care to many poor people in these countries who would otherwise not receive the care they need.

There was one young lad from Bolivia whose family had disowned him because he was blind and of no use to them. He came here and we took care of his cataracts. Now he has been welcomed back to his family and is continuing with his life.

Mary Toma
– Executive Vice President and Chief Operating Officer
– Vice President of Patient Care Services

I attended Alverno College in Milwaukee and graduated with a bachelors degree in nursing in 1964. I then earned my masters degree in health services and administration from the University of St. Francis.

Recently, I completed the steps necessary to progress within the American College of Healthcare Executives to Fellow status. So now I am a Fellow of the College, effective in November, 1998. First, you become an Associate, then you're a Diplomate and you have to wait five years before you can become a Fellow of the College – that's the highest status that you can attain in the College.

I came to NAH in 1974 as the Director of Nurses. In 1987, I was appointed Vice President of Patient Care Services, which meant that I had all the nursing and the clinical support services under my supervision. This included radiology, lab, pharmacy, food services, respiratory services and several other areas.

In '91 I was promoted to Executive Vice President and Chief Operating Officer. From that time, all hospital departments report to me except for the finance department, who report to the chief financial officer, including Information

Systems and Medical Records. He in turn reports to the C.E.O. All other departments are within the scope of my responsibility including the ten satellite clinics that serve the surrounding community – the ProHealth Clinics. I have recently taken over the administrative responsibility for Continuing Medical Education for the doctors, as well as the medical library and medical students. We provide podiatry students training in this hospital and we're in the process of developing a Family Practice residency, which we hope to implement by late 1999 or early 2000.

We have about 700 employees of which about 295 are in nursing, so the nursing staff makes up almost half of the total number of employees.

Our current length of stay – that is, the average number of days the patient stays in the hospital, is about 3.5 days. Actually, when I started we had a very big OB department. However, the surrounding community has aged since I came here in '74. We had nearly 4,300 deliveries one year, which was a message that the people around the hospital were very young. Over the years, those who have remained in the community have gotten older, so now we are tending to see a higher percentage of Medicare patients and that tends to raise the average length of stay because when a Mom comes in to have her baby, assuming that she is well, she's in one day and out the next with the baby. When older people are admitted, they are usually sicker, with more bodily systems involved so that they stay longer. We will have to be certain that our length of stay remains within national standards.

Right now we have about 20 percent Medicare patients. We're at a length of stay of 3.5 days compared with a length of stay of 2.8 days before. When we look at other hospitals, they are running 6 and 6.5 average length of stays because they have many Medicare patients. We are trying to increase our Medicare patients. That will help to insure our profitability.

We currently are running about 50 percent Medicaid (public aid) patients.

That's down a bit. In the past it used to be higher because then Governor Edgar tried to move the Medicaid population into managed care, and some of this has happened. Medicaid patient numbers have gone down and managed care numbers have increased.

As far as nursing at this hospital is concerned, we have little turnover and we definitely promote recruitment of bilingual nurses because of our patient population. We have been fairly successful at that. Nursing managers are all credentialed in their specialties. For example, we have one manager in the maternity area who is credentialed by the American Nurses Association in that specialty. Increasingly we are having our nurses credentialed in their specialties. Hopefully, the majority will be credentialed by the year 2000.

Regarding longevity, I would say NAH does better than other hospitals. For example, we have a nurse here who is leaving at the end of the year after working 41 years in the nursery. I was here 25 years in March, 1999. When I look around, I see many of the people that I hired still working here, which tells me that our longevity record is good.

I was hired by a former administrator who had been here for many years. Through the years that this former administrator was in charge, I reported to him but saw him infrequently. In 1982 National Medical Enterprises came in with a new administrator, Mr. Leyhe, and that changed everything. There were meetings and more meetings and we had a nurse consultant from National Medical Enterprises who came here every three months. Each time she would review the performance of nursing. The hospital was managed until '87 or so. It was quite a change in our operations. The new group turned the hospital around financially.

I learned a lot from Mr. Leyhe. He was very astute. Then Brim and Associates took over and they sent us Mr. Sussman. He was here from '87 to '90 or '91, at which time the Board decided not to renew our contract with Brim. At that time the Board appointed the former administrator as President and I became Executive Vice President and Chief Operating Officer. That's how it's been since then.

We stay because there's quite a challenge here, for example, the new accountability and new standards to shoot for that came in when NME was here, which is quite different than what it had been under the previous administrator.

When Mr. Leyhe was here he worked very hard and we all were motivated by him, because we had a strategic plan for the hospital to shoot for. As time went by and I was promoted several times, the question was why I would look elsewhere when I was growing with the organization.

When Mr. Dahl became Chairman of the Board, we adopted the family logo – the father standing behind the mother with the child. Mr. Dahl has tried to instill, and I believe successfully, a family spirit here at Norwegian, starting with the

Board, our medical staff, management and of course our employees. Nowadays when our former Chairman, Mr. Dahl or other members of the Board need to use the pharmacy or lab for service our employees know them. When I started here, you wouldn't know any Board member because there was no contact between the Board and the employees. At that time the only one that attended the Board meetings was the former administrator.

But when Mr. Leyhe came, I started to attend the Board meetings, as did the Chief Financial Officer and the Administrator. We still do. We have warmer working relationships. The Board philosophy is expressed as family oriented and that made the hospital a rather nice place in which to work.

To a certain degree our community is changing. Today when I go through the lobby, I see a lot of African Americans. We are going to have to be sensitive to that insofar as when patients are admitted we keep our African Americans and Hispanics separate. That way we avoid such problems as TV sets which are set for Spanish speaking. Our African American patients cannot understand Spanish.

Currently, we are upgrading the interior of the hospital, remodeling unit by unit. For example, we are remodeling our ICU (Intensive Care Unit) on the fourth floor, which was too small and the Joint Commission on Healthcare recommended that this unit be expanded. We went from 8 beds to 12 beds, with the very latest technology.

One of our strengths is that we are trying to offer the highest technology. However, we are not a tertiary care center by design. We are a community hospital serving the community and our affiliation with Illinois Masonic Hospital gives us a nice bridge to use in case we have a very sick patient that needs care we can't provide. We send them our critically ill babies and they send them back to us when they get better.

For the future, one of our challenges is to recruit more doctors. Our medical staff is aging. It averages in the mid-50s or so. We have to recruit new physicians to replace them. We are moving aggressively in that direction. One of the reasons we are initiating a Family Practice residency is to encourage some of the residents to stay with the hospital after they complete their training.

Clarence Nagelvoort – Former President and Chief Executive Officer

In March of 2000, Clarence Nagelvoort, hospital President and Chief Executive Officer since 1992, announced his resignation from the staff.

I received my bachelor of science in pharmacy at the University of Illinois in 1979 and my masters degree in business administration at the U of I in 1985. I came to NAH in '81 as the Director of Pharmacy. I previously had worked for Jewel Osco in their manage-ment development program for a year and a half after I got out of school.

I should also mention that while attending pharmacy school, I took a sequence in management – a pharmacy management program – and then I completed a formal program in business management at the University. I also had a position in the adjunct faculty at the U of I and worked at several other hospitals part-time for additional experience. These included Rush-Presbyterian-St. Luke's and Good Samaritan in Downers Grove.

In 1991 I became Vice President of the hospital and in the Fall of '91 I was appointed the Executive Vice President of NAH and that's when the management contract with Brim ended. Then I became the President of the hospital in '92 and have remained in that capacity until my recent resignation.

The major changes that I have seen here since I started include the strong improvements in the clinical departments of the hospital. The contract with NME started in '82, about a year after I started here, and that certainly was a major change.

In '83 the federal government installed a revised payment system that made it very difficult for hospitals to operate – the so-called DRG system, in which hospitals were paid on the diagnosis, so much per patient for the diagnosis, and if the patient care exceeded that amount, the hospital had to pay the excess out of its own funds.

This put a tremendous hardship on hospitals and this was the time that you began to see hospitals closing in Chicago. All throughout the '80s you saw hospitals closing because of these changes – including right here in this area, Walther Memorial, St. Anne's, Mary Thompson, Martha Washington, and Henrotin. There were many reasons that these hospitals closed, but in general there were so many difficulties in getting paid, which was part of a federal government program, that the hospitals that closed could not adapt to this.

Everybody lost money in those years on Medicaid. It was a very bad system.

Today we probably do not lose money on Medicaid, but it did cause a lot of hardship for the hospital.

We have of course other sources of income besides Medicaid, but that was a very big source of income with perhaps 50 percent of our patients on Medicaid and it has been pretty steady around that figure for the past few years.

Another major change was that in the '80s, the hospital started buying property in the surrounding area. In the years '85 and '86, we started to buy buildings in the area, and installing parks and improving the area and getting rid of crack houses nearby and other rundown properties. This made for a greener parkway area and we also installed a safety and security net around the hospital that continues to this day. Most of the later development occurred in the years – '91 and '92 through '93 with the development of the parking lots, the promenade leading to the parks, and of course our new Professional Building, for which I credit our former Board Chairman Norm Dahl. Mr. Dahl led the way in obtaining these properties and making this all happen. We had many barriers in acquiring these properties, including some property on Division Street which was across the street from the current church, but Norm hung in there and we eventually did obtain it.

Starting in '92, we completed our new surgery unit – a brand new surgery wing which had not been changed since the '30s, and then in '93 we built our new emergency room, both of which were major improvements.

But the primary change since I joined the hospital staff, where we experienced considerable payment restrictions and reductions, was the improvement in management of department areas. I volunteered to take on more responsibility and to take on management of other departments as well as my own. And besides all of this, I at one point had the responsibility for the construction program, and the insurance program. And I learned management of all of these major areas of the hospital through hands-on experience.

Other major improvements or changes that have occurred in our operations are referred to in Chapter 11, which deals with future planning and concerns. For one, this refers to our recent agreement with Illinois Masonic which provides care for our patients which we presently cannot provide, and our excellent relations with the medical staff.

The major challenge of the future, as I see it, is to be aware of what is happening around you, being able to somewhat predict in order to control the destiny of the hospital. Some risks must be taken. It's very important that we do so. Clearly, in the future we must be focused on the quality of patient care as well as the hospital financial responsibility.

In recent years we have had the tremendous benefit of technology, enabling us to offer services and care that were inconceivable only a few years ago. And this in turn has lessened the needs in many ways of traditional hospital services. On the other hand, we have an aging population. We are going to have more seniors in the next 30 years than we have ever seen in the United States before and these people will need care, so there will be less extra capacity in the hospital than there is now.

The current trend will certainly continue to minimize the use of hospitals. The hospitals are no longer just hospitals – they are healthcare institutions in that they provide a lot of outpatient care, such as kidney dialysis, emergency care and treatment, physical therapy, and so forth.

Hospitals will also serve other functions besides providing beds for the very sick. They are the only part of the healthcare system that can really provide the capital required to finance the cost of these new technologies. There have been some successful physician generated joint ventures, but typically the hospitals have had to carry the weight of these innovations. Physicians, or groups of physicians, cannot expend the amount of money required to provide this new technology, which can mount into many millions of dollars.

This includes new and better imaging equipment, further improvements in ultrasound for example, MRI technology, etc. You will see more and more non-invasive imaging in cardiology and you will see a boom in organ transplants twenty years from now. We will arrive at the point where when you are 90, you'll simply have all of your major organs replaced, which will enable you to live for 20 or 30 years longer.

We have a new procedure in open heart surgery for instance which allows surgeons to bypass the plugged up arteries through the use of a very slight incision in the chest, whereas formerly they had to saw through the breastbone and open up the chest in order to get to the heart.

The future will certainly be challenging and those hospitals that do not become complacent and which are willing to put in the effort and work, will be successful.

I am confident that our hospital will succeed in the future because it is focused in the right places – on the needs of the community as well as the needs of the physicians and the patients. We are looking at how to support the clinical staff to provide this care and the Board will provide the overall supervision to offer the necessary structure and control to accomplish this. If we work hard and continue to improve our services, then we will always be needed and we will be successful.

For example, if we build a new hospital, there would be fewer beds and more space for outpatient care. But we should also consider that if we have a brand new surgery wing and a new emergency room, that it would be impractical to build a new hospital right away. But if we accumulate the funds at the next point where technology and modernization are called for, we should be up-to-date on everything at one time. We are building a new ICU right now.

Our current building will never be allowed to deteriorate. But the layout is difficult. You have newer services in the old building but it's harder to reconfigure this hospital because it consists of four separate buildings all joined together into one. You have four separate structural systems, you have twelve different heating and cooling systems, you have energy requirements in systems that are not efficient so that may become an issue.

The main issue is that we have current management that is aware of the tradition and history of this hospital. I think we have done a good job in making the hospital stronger and carrying the torch forward for the next generation of those who will use the hospital.

Norman R. Dahl
– Former Chairman of the Board,
Norwegian American Hospital

I joined the Board in 1965 so I've been on the Board for 35 years, and had served as chairman of the Board for the past 10 years.

I joined the Board at the invitation of Marshall Pedersen, who was a Director here and a member of the Northwest Lions Club, who told me at a meeting of a local Norwegian group, the Normennenes Singing Society, one night that it was time that I should do something for the Norwegian community. He had reference to Norwegian American Hospital and felt that I could make a contribution here.

I attended my first Board meeting then and was not really that interested and was thinking of resigning, when D. Lundy, who was a member of the Oak Park Lions Club, as was I, and who was Chairman of the hospital Board, prevailed upon me to continue on the Board and asked that I try to take a more active role. I told him that I would do this and that was the beginning of my long relationship with NAH. Then when John P. Iversen was Chairman, he asked that I handle the committee on employee affairs and that was the beginning of my involvement in the hospital and from there I was elected a Vice-Chairman of the Board and then Chairman of the Hospital. And I changed the entire structure of the Board and the hospital management for they were living in the past.

Under the changes I instituted, the Chairman of the Board is a corporate officer as is the Treasurer and the Secretary. There was a lot of debate and some were upset including the previous Treasurer because he felt that we were taking away his office and putting it on the corporate side. So now these officers are part of management, while the members of the Board continue to set overall policy.

The executive administrator became the president and the chief executive officer and the financial vice president became the chief financial officer and the operating officer was made the chief operating officer. We restructured the Board to make room for placing more management people in an executive role.

And from this came other challenges over the years and there were four physicians on the Board at the time who would always do the opposite of what the rest of the Board wanted to do. There were three hospital-based physicians and one admitting physician who were more of an obstacle to what we wanted to accomplish than anything else. So the next challenge was to replace them with physicians who admitted patients and this we accomplished.

Another change that we made was done while Mike Sussman was still administrator and that was a restructuring of our affiliate corporations and the development of a parent corporation called Norwegian American Health Systems, under which the hospital is a subsidiary as well as the Foundation, and the Community Trust Fund, which formerly were all separate corporations, now became subsidiaries of the parent corporation, Norwegian American Health Systems. Also we changed the name of the Women's Auxiliary to the Woman's Board and gave them a structure that would allow them to generate funds.

When Mr. Sussman left, we interviewed many candidates for the position of CEO and President. Those that were most acceptable wanted more than we could pay and those that were not acceptable were not employed and hence not worth too much to us. Ultimately, we asked the operating president to take over the chief executive's job but he committed some serious mistakes when he sought to convert our existing dental operatories into a waiting room. That was promptly remedied and today we have four income-producing operatories instead of two, as well as an oral surgery suite. At the time, there was no one on the outside that was acceptable and we decided to promote from within and I stayed on as Chairman.

All this time we managed to stay afloat when several hospitals in the area went under, including the hospital that was directly across the park from us. Our approach was to give real meaning to the expression that the physician is our best customer and we have always tried to give the doctors the respect they deserve and we have tried to make them feel that they were needed in this hospital. Once that message penetrated, the physicians really felt that they were part of the hospital. We instituted an open door policy for all doctors unless of course the administrator was meeting in private with someone.

Besides making all of these changes, I said early on that if the hospital is to survive, it must be progressive. I'm not talking about bricks and mortar. I refer to our policies on healthcare. The bricks and mortar will follow if the healthcare of our constituents is recognized by starting new services, for example the dental suite, which has been expanded as I noted above. We also have a pedodontist to handle the dental needs of children and we have a periodontist, who handles gum disease and an orthodontist, who straightens out teeth as well as the above mentioned oral surgeon. So we have a complete dental service here and it's generating revenue and showing a profit.

Another example is the Women's Center, and we have expanded the Doctors Specialty Area (outpatient center) and the emergency room has been expanded by nearly 100 percent. The operating room has been completely revamped and expanded, with new lighting and equipment. And the OB department has been expanded as well. All of these changes in our services are based on the expressed needs of community residents. And I should mention that we are doing more and more one-day surgery too.

Take our surgery suite. We now have five state-of-the-art operating rooms, and we are in the process of expanding the ICU, which will have the latest technology as recommended by the Joint Commission, which approves hospitals to make sure they comply with hospital regulations.

And even before all of these changes and new services were made, there was some concern by the doctors that some of the patients coming here at night were afraid to come here because the area was dark. So we acquired all of the surrounding buildings and developed these into a campus which is open and well lit.

Later it became apparent that we had to change the image presented by the hospital's appearance, which was grim and resembled a factory, so we built the new Professional Office Building with new entrances on both Thomas and Cortez Streets instead of the old entrance on Francisco.

The professional building is completely occupied and provides rental space for those who want it. The $11 million it cost to build is entirely paid. There is no mortgage and the debt that we had when I first joined the Board is gone and we still have the reserves to provide the funds to carry us if need be.

Looking to the future, our expertise is in the area of the newborns – which peaked at 4,300 several years ago and is now less than 3,000 a year, but we expect that that will once again rise in the near future since mothers who have had their babies here will return because they know that this is our strength.

And we've got an outstanding medical staff here. We've expanded the oncology clinic. In addition to our dental program, we have the Women's Health Center oncology program. We've acquired ten clinics in outlying areas – our ProHealth Satellite clinics.

In the past five years we have poured about $20 million into the area, plus the $11 million that we invested in the Professional Office Building – in other words, more than $30 million. And this has all been made possible through expert management.

For the future, as the need arises, we're going to have to raise a sizeable amount of money to build a new hospital. It will focus on outpatient care, one-day surgery, emergency health care and so forth – about 100 beds or less for acutely ill patients.

We're looking at a cost of $75 to $80 million, not including the land. This will probably happen within the next five years. The new unit would be located just north of our present site and would be bound by Division Street on the north and Thomas Street on the south. This will be something that we must be ready to implement, but it's hard to say just when we will proceed with this. It may not happen during my lifetime, but at least the planning will be done – the land will be cleared and we will be able to go ahead with it if need be. We have already acquired most of the 40 or so buildings that we will need to go ahead. So we already have about 75 percent of the land that we need and the address of the building would be 2901 W. Division Street.

As to our present structure, we may use that as an extended care facility, as a nursing home for those suffering from such debilitating diseases as cancer or stroke. The building could easily be converted into such a facility.

The Board needs to address this issue – to build a new hospital if the need arises. As an active member of the Lions Club, we apply this principle to whatever programs we undertake. We first attempt to address the needs of the community and then to find ways and means of meeting those needs. In the same manner as the Lions Club, we are attempting to determine the needs of the hospital through our strategic planning. And from this plan, we can determine when we have to look to the future in developing a new plant to service the hospital.

The hospital boilers for example need replacement. We must build a new power plant for the hospital to provide the energy that we will need. We now have access to California, to Sacramento and to Division – all of the area we need except for Augusta Boulevard. We lack about three buildings for this to happen and when we acquire these, we will have the entire area from Division to Augusta and from the west side of Richmond to Francisco.

The Foundation is designed to support the needs of the hospital. It currently has about $1.5 million in assets. I would like to see it reach $6 million in the next five years and the earnings siphoned off to meet the immediate needs of the hospital.

In summary then, the hospital has survived at least two great crises, the first stemming from the Depression and the second from the changes in reimbursement for healthcare, due largely to government restrictions and the problems that we run into involving HMO's and managed care in general. These problems will continue to challenge us in the future and we must be careful not to fall asleep at the switch – we will have to keep our fingers on the pulse of what is going on in healthcare. Otherwise we will lose out.

EXHIBIT 2

Great Men and Women of Medicine at Norwegian American Hospital

The section which follows profiles some of the distinguished men and women who joined the staff of the fledgling Norwegian Lutheran Tabitha Hospital (as it was originally known) after it opened in 1893 and who were involved with the hospital in various capacities over the years.

Dr. Christian Fenger

Perhaps the outstanding doctor practicing in Chicago at the end of the 19th century was Dr. Christian Fenger, after whom a high school in Chicago is named, and whose story reads almost like a page out of an adventure novel. Danish by birth, Dr. Fenger was one of twelve children born to Kammeraad and Frederikke Fenger in 1840.

Originally intending to become a civil engineer, young Fenger in 1860 yielded to his father's wishes and enrolled at the Polyteknisk Laeareanstalt to study medicine. To help pay for his tuition he taught anatomy to medical students and later coached dental students in their studies.

Following a war with Prussia in which Danes yielded the territories of Schleswig-Holstein to Prussia, Fenger passed the final exams allowing him to practice medicine, with high marks.

From 1869 to 1871 he interned in surgery at Royal Frederick's Hospital. During this period his experiments in gunshot wounds of horses at the Royal Veterinary College and a paper he wrote on his work, "Concerning the Endoscopy of Gunshot Wounds," led to a grant from the Royal Danish Ministry of War which he used to further his studies during the Franco-German War of 1871.

After the war he studied pathologic anatomy and surgery in Vienna, returning to Denmark in late 1870, where he wrote his thesis for the medical degree on: "Cancer of the Stomach."

In 1875 when one of the professors at the academy took sick, he filled in by instructing the students in pathologic anatomy. Following a disappointment in a professorship which failed to materialize, he joined his brother, Dr. Sophus Fenger in Alexandria, Egypt in 1875 taking over his brother's practice temporarily when the latter returned to Denmark in order to be married. He later became a member of the Board of Health of Cairo, where he studied trachoma, a condition prevalent in the eyes of many Egyptian children at the time.

After being felled by a liver disease which necessitated his removal to a cooler climate, he wound up in Chicago in the Spring of 1878, where he obtained a position as a professor at Cook County Hospital. There he gave lectures and demonstrations on pathologic anatomy, a science which he described as "unknown to the physicians there" at the time.

He was at Cook County for a total of 14 years, first as pathologist and later as surgeon, and among others he is credited with introducing Lister's antiseptic methods at the hospital.

In 1880 he became curator of Rush Medical College museum; in 1884 professor of surgery at the College of Physicians and Surgeons and Surgeon in Chief at Passavant Hospital. This was followed by an appointment as professor of surgery at Chicago Medical College, later Northwestern Medical School. Then in 1899 he left Northwestern to assume the post of Professor of Surgery at Rush Medical College, then affiliated with the University of Chicago. It was during this period, in 1894 that he became affiliated with the then Norwegian Lutheran Tabitha Hospital, where for a brief period he followed the eminent Dr. Karl Sandberg, as surgeon in chief.

In the course of his 24 years in Chicago he wrote dozens of articles which were published in the medical press. Then in 1895 he became Vice President of the

American Surgical Association and in 1901 President of the Chicago Medical Society and the Chicago Surgical Society.

In 1900, on the occasion of his 60th birthday, he was given a testimonial banquet which was attended by more than 500 friends, physicians, and students. At the time he was presented with a loving cup on which was engraved his portrait, and an album from the celebrated surgeon, Nicholas Senn, his colleague at Rush Medical College, containing the autograms of many of those present. Then in 1902 he was honored with the Royal Order of Dannebrog from King Christian IX.

Fenger enjoyed a phenomenal reputation as a surgeon and a pathologist which extended far beyond Chicago. Patients and students from all over the country and for that matter, all over the world, sought his advice. He died in Chicago in 1902.

Dr. Ludvig Hektoen

One of Norwegian American Hospital's earliest distinguished men of medicine, Dr. Ludvig Hektoen, was born near LaCrosse, Wisconsin in 1863, of Norwegian immigrant parents who were farmers.

At the tender age of 16, Hektoen enrolled at Luther College, in Decorah, Iowa, where he received a B.A. at the age of 20. He then entered what was then the College of Physicians and Surgeons (later the University of Illinois Medical College) receiving his M.D. degree in 1887.

After taking first place in the intern's examination at Cook County Hospital, he came down with an infection, which William K. Beatty, in a paper published in the Institute of Medicine in 1982, said was treated by none other than Christian Fenger, the hospital's pioneering pathologist. Not only did the great doctor treat Hektoen's illness, but he thoughtfully wrote to Hektoen's father stating that his son would recover and he went on to train Hektoen as a pathologist and encouraged him to enter the field. In 1895, the hospital appointed Hektoen pathologist, a post he held for eight years.

Young Hektoen could be bluntly outspoken in his efforts to improve sanitary conditions at the hospital, Beatty writes, quoting Hektoen as follows: "...The sanitary condition of the ward is imperfect; the sewerage is bad and during the rain, water leaks through the ceiling in torrents into the ...lying in ward especially and then to the ward...below. Attention of the authorities have been directed to these defects over a month ago and until they are remedied a perfectly normal course of the lying-in period cannot be hoped for."

"While Hektoen's writing style later improved," comments Beatty, "he never lost his anger at thoughtlessness and political greed."

Following his internship, he started an active practice of medicine and in 1890 he was appointed coroner's physician, serving in that capacity until 1894.

Writing in the March 1949 *Lamp*, after Dr. Hektoen had served on the Norwegian American Board for more than 25 years, Dr. Manuel Lichtenstein, a distinguished surgeon in his own right, wrote: "His interest in pathology was stimulated by his studies during the year 1890 at various European places of learning-including Uppsala, Berlin, and Prague."

Then after serving as professor of pathology at Rush Medical College for three years, he was appointed professor and head of the department of Pathology at the University of Chicago in 1901. And the following year the newly formed John McCormick Institute of Infectious Diseases chose him as director. Hektoen held each of these positions for more than 30 years.

Beatty writes that "Hektoen's association with the Institute became not only peculiarly satisfying to him, but also a textbook example of a successful memorial...where he could engage in challenging research as well as train and encourage other investigators."

The Institute had been established, comments Beatty, primarily as a memorial to the young son of Harold and Edith Rockefeller McCormick, who had died of scarlet fever. Working under Hektoen's leadership, primarily through the research of George and Gladys Dick, the Institute ultimately established the cause of the disease, and developed a skin test to determine susceptibility to the disease, as well as a method of immunization and a specific antitoxin for its treatment.

In 1905 Hektoen reported the experimental transmission of measles in humans and he made a major breakthrough when he became the first scientist to suggest that proper selection of blood donors could remove most of the dangers then involved in the new field of blood transfusion.

"Each of these achievements was important in itself, "writes Lichtenstein, "but one will be remembered beyond the close of the century – Hektoen's discovery in 1907 of the principle of cross matching of blood before transfusion. Thanks to this discovery, blood transfusion was made safe and certain.

"...Hektoen insisted upon adequate controls and prolonged observation, checking and rechecking of all experiments. He was cautious of the worker who found what he sought. He demanded thorough acquaintance with the literature...."

"The McCormick Institute achieved the purpose for which it was established and more," writes Lichtenstein. "It set the course for scientific investigation both here and abroad."

Besides being a born investigator, Beatty writes, "Hektoen was an accomplished teacher. He became the first in Chicago (and probably in the United States) to do blood cultures to determine the presence of disease."

The broad areas of cancer and public health were particular concerns of his, and in 1930 he became chairman of the Cancer Research Institute of Chicago and founder of the Chicago Tumor Institute.

Add to all of these attributes, Hektoen's high regard for order and organization. "He never cluttered his desk with piles of unanswered letters and unread journals and books," Beatty writes, adding, "...This attention to detail and method showed itself not only in his research but also in his writing and editorial labors."

In 1899, Hektoen became a finalist among the candidates for the editorship of the *Journal of the American Medical Association* and indeed he did contribute editorials to the *Journal* for more than 40 years.

In 1904 he became founder and first editor of the *Journal of Infectious Diseases*, a journal which won high fame during Hektoen's 36 years in its editor's chair. Hektoen's own articles, essays and editorials, numbering more than 300, ranged over many subjects and several of these articles are still being used.

To have such an outstanding researcher, clinician and teacher on the staff of Norwegian American was especially noteworthy. Hektoen was for several decades active on the Board of Trustees of Norwegian American Hospital and his contribution, especially during its critical formative years around the turn of the century, cannot be measured. "As a memorial to this worthy man of medicine," Lichtenstein writes, "our laboratory continues to bear the name Hektoen Memorial Laboratory."

During his lifetime Hektoen achieved numerous honors. He was for several years the president of the Chicago Surgical Society and in 1903 was elected president of the American Pathologists and Bacteriologists. He was president of the Chicago Medical Society in 1920-21.

His many honors included election to the National Academy of Sciences (1918); the Order of St. Olaw (1929) from the Norwegian government; and the Distinguished Service Medal of the American Medical Association. He died in 1951 at the age of 88.

Dr. Lichtenstein sums up Dr. Hektoen's life in one highly descriptive paragraph as follows: "Hektoen, through his work at the Institute and other medical institutions, taught a single unforgettable lesson that the worth of an institution lies not in its numerous buildings, its spacious grounds, its vast wealth nor its numerous grants, but rests alone in a free and flexible environment...In our obligation to produce research people of the highest quality, the problem of our age is how we can bring out talent, how we can influence youth with the passion to seek out new knowledge, how we can develop talent. History affords the answer. The McCormick Institute, since renamed in honor of Ludvig Hektoen, gives a suggestion."

Dr. Anton J. Carlson

"Scientist, philosopher, teacher, and humanist, Dr. Anton J. Carlson, during his lifetime made an unforgettable contribution to his adopted country, his fellow scientists and the medical profession," writes Dr. Manuel Lichtenstein, one of the great men of medicine at Norwegian American Hospital, in an article appearing in the Spring 1970 issue of the *Lamp*.

"Dr. Carlson's gift for keen analysis, his ready wit and pungent criticism, so often displayed at scientific meetings and a number of lectures at Norwegian American Hospital, gave him an acknowledged place in many biological and medical societies," Dr. Lichtenstein writes. "In fact he was so well regarded by his contemporaries that he was voted an honorary membership of the Norwegian American medical staff," he continues.

Born on a small farm in Sweden in 1875, his father died tragically while he was a toddler and at age seven he was spending his summers working as a sheepherder.

During the long winter months, he tramped two miles through the snowdrifts to a country schoolhouse where he spent the evenings doing housework and learning how to knit his own wool stockings.

While still in his teens, Carlson, joined his brother Albin, a sailor, in setting out for the New World and in March 1891 after arriving in Chicago, he started to work as a carpenter's helper. Before long he was persuaded by a local minister to put aside his tools and enroll in the Augustana Academy and College in Rock Island where by 1898 he obtained his B.A. degree.

Originally planning to join the ministry, young Carlson actually served as substitute minister in Anaconda, Montana for about a year, before deciding that he really wanted to explore the human nervous system and he decided to become a physiologist.

After receiving his Ph.D. degree in physiology from Stanford University in 1902, Dr. Carlson was appointed a research assistant at the Carnegie Technical Institute. And it was while there that he conducted his renowned experiments on the prevalent theories concerning the conduction of the cardiac impulse.

Then in 1894, he was offered the position of associate in the physiology department at the University of Chicago, where he remained the rest of his life. He started his work as an assistant professor and later was appointed professor and chairman of the department of physiology.

Enlisting as a captain at the outbreak of World War I, Dr. Carlson worked in the newly organized Sanitary Corps, where he eventually went off to England and then to France as a quality inspector, to inspect the quality of food served in Army camps.

At the close of World War I, he was appointed by President Hoover to head a humanitarian commission with the objective of feeding the starving children of the defeated countries.

Returning to Chicago, Dr. Carlson for the next 20 years directed experimental research of many graduate students at the University of Chicago. He was also involved in public health devoting considerable time and energy to helping secure free lunches for poor children in Chicago's public schools.

In 1946, the American Medical Association awarded him its highest honor, the Distinguished Humanist award, and almost at the very same time, he received the Humanist of the Year award of the American Humanist Association.

He died in 1956 and his epitaph might well have been the words that follow, written during a trying period of the nation's history. "Even in the face of current fears and pessimism that during the ups and downs of the past million years, man has gradually acquired more understanding, more freedom from fear, more dignity, greater kindness and clearer conception of justice. Even though for the moment the bird of sorrow is not only flying over our heads but is actually nesting in our hair...that bird will not nest in our hair forever unless a blackout of science be decreed...for slowly but surely the understanding of man provided by science will help to make our lives more intelligent, toil more cheerful, fear and hatred, pain and tears less prevalent in our lives."

Dr. John V. Fowler, Sr.

There have been many great and dedicated men in our past. But few have contributed more to the medical stature and the growth of our hospital in its early years than Dr. John Vanus Fowler, surgeon, teacher, and organizer extraordinaire.

Proving to be the exception to the rule of the virtually entirely Scandinavian medical staff that characterized Norwegian American Hospital during its critical early years, Fowler was born to Rachel and Frank Fowler in 1869. His father, a former confederate army captain, had been wounded in the battle of Murfreesboro.

Fowler was born and raised in the foothills of the Cumberland Mountains where his father, a stern, strong-minded individual, never permitted smoking, alcohol, profanity or card playing.

The story is told that when Frank Fowler was a prisoner, he was lined up with the others and forced to vote for Abe Lincoln, an event which so incensed him that he swore to never vote again, and he held to his promise.

Young Fowler spent most of his boyhood in Buffalo, Missouri, a tiny hamlet in the Ozarks and a favorite haunt of many train robbers including the James brothers.

In 1888, Fowler entered Valparaiso University, receiving his bachelor's degree four years later. From 1892 to 1895 he was the principal of a new high school in Hallock, Minnesota.

An amusing anecdote is told of Fowler of this period in his life, noting that it was his habit to carry a gun. While accompanying a minister acquaintance on a walk one Sunday afternoon, they came upon a band of young boys throwing rocks at a prairie chicken. Dr. Fowler quickly extricated his revolver and with one shot caused the head and the body of the chicken to part company. The stunned minister told Fowler in no uncertain terms that it was considered bad taste in Minnesota for a high school principal to "pack a gun." Needless to say, Fowler had little trouble with rowdies in his high school classes.

In 1895, John Fowler decided to enroll at Rush Medical College of Chicago graduating in 1899 as a surgeon. During his last year of medical school he worked evenings for a Dr. Strong, later taking over Dr. Strong's practice at Grand and Elizabeth Street when Dr. Strong died.

Early on in his medical career he was appointed the doctor for the Chicago & Northwestern Railroad and worked in his spare time at the Central Free Dispensary of Rush Medical College. He was also associated with the Chicago College of Medicine and Surgery (later Loyola University Medical School) where he taught anatomy and surgery.

In 1909 he was appointed clinical professor of surgery at the College, a post he held until 1918 when he became president of the Chicago Medical Society.

In the early days he was renowned for his skill in intubating cases of diphtheria, then epidemic in the city. For a while he was on the staff of four community hospitals: Frances Willard, Lutheran Deaconess, St. Elizabeth and Norwegian American, before deciding to limit his practice to NAH in 1918.

It was at Norwegian that he started daily clinical conferences that continued for 25 years and since Norwegian was the only private hospital in the country to have such a teaching program for both its staff physicians and interns, many famous physicians appeared on the NAH lectern.

Dr. Fowler was a great organizer as well as surgeon and in 1903 he became a member of the Chicago Medical Society and one of the founders of the Northwest Branch. After many active roles in the Society, he became its secretary in 1916 and president in 1929. In all he held office continuously in the Society for 40 years.

In 1942, he and his wife the former Bertha Griffiths, a former nurse at Presbyterian Hospital, moved to Florida where they spent their winters, returning to Chicago during the summertime. After Mrs. Fowler's death in 1954 he returned to Chicago. In 1958, while visiting friends in Florida, he broke his hip and was flown back to Norwegian American Hospital for treatment. He remained at the hospital, near his many friends and associates, until he died in 1962 at the age of 92. His two sons, John and Frank, were both on the medical staff of Norwegian American at one time or another.

Helga Ruud

"Who can forget that peppery Helga Ruud?" so begins an article appearing in the Summer 1970 issue of the *Lamp* by Dr. Larsandrew Dolan. "She was unforgettable and I can still see the doctors sit up and take notice when she presented one of her papers at staff meetings," Dr. Dolan writes.

Born in Kongsberg, Norway in 1860, she came to America at the age of 18 to take a post as governess with a family in Iowa, which paid the handsome salary of $100 a year. She soon obtained similar employment with a colonel in the U.S. Army and spent the next five years moving around the country from one army post to another.

But always there burned within her a fierce desire to do something positive with her life and she decided that being a physician would help her to attain her goals. She enrolled in the Women's College of Medicine, then affiliated with Northwestern University in 1889, when women who entered the field were looked on with great skepticism.

"With her meager formal training, but a good, clear thinking mind and much energy," Dr. Dolan writes, "she always kept up with the advances of medicine and still found time to teach at Northwestern from 1897 to 1901."

She was associated with the Norwegian American Hospital School of Nursing as an instructor for 34 years and still found time to become president of the Medical Women's Club and the Women's Clinical Dispensary.

Subsequently she helped organize and became the first president of the Norwegian Women's Federation, in which she was active almost up until her death.

On the 50th anniversary of her becoming a physician, the Chicago Medical Society presented her with a gold pin, the Norwegian American Hospital held a reception for her and the Federation hosted a large celebration in her honor.

Following her retirement, Dr. Ruud found time to write a history of women in medicine for each state in the Union. Only Dr. Ruud could have been chosen for Illinois.

Dr. Ruud dedicated herself to the cause of peace, writes Dr. Dolan, adding that "she declared herself unequivocally and always a pacifist and was for total and absolute world disarmament. Thus she lived for nearly a hundred years by the time of her death in 1956, and it was an orderly, progressive, humanitarian life, not tarnished by avoiding issues, but inspired because she faced them head on with energy. She never sacrificed honesty and forthrightness for polite evasion."

"The world is a much better place because of Dr. Helga Ruud..." Dr. Dolan concludes.

Birger Osland

During the trying days of the Depression, Birger Osland, then Chairman of the Board is credited with almost singlehandedly leading the hospital out of the whirlpool of economic ruin and collapse which swirled around it in the early '30s through the early '40s:

"Many great men have helped forge the history of our hospital, but none played a greater role or made a greater contribution. A financier and humanitarian rather than a man of medicine, he was a member of our Board of Trustees for 41 years and served as president from 1937 to 1948 during some of the hospital's most trying times," wrote the late Dr. Manuel Lichtenstein, a great surgeon at Norwegian American Hospital from 1935 to 1971, who knew Osland well during his years as Board member and later chairman of the Board.

When things had been straightened out with victory over the considerable financial difficulties, he charted the hospital's future with these words: "During these times our friendship and loyalty have been put to a severe test, but we have won again. Let our aim remain the same: to continue to serve the people in a friendly manner with the finest professional talent, the best equipment and the most careful service."

That the hospital had triumphed over its seemingly insurmountable problems is indeed true and it was due primarily to Osland's courage and never flagging determination that it was able to do so.

Born in Stavanger, Norway in 1870, Osland came to this country in 1888 arriving in Chicago in August of that year with six dollars in his pocket. In his book, *A Long Pull from Stavanger*, Osland describes the Chicago of that time with railroads, horsedrawn street cars, factories, soot, smoke and stockyard smells. But it was alive and this fired his imagination with hope and conviction.

His first job was as a waiter and a dishwasher at a Danish restaurant at the grand total of $3.50 per week and meals. Next came a stint as a buffer wheel operator in a nickel plating shop, and then a job in which he joined the office force of the Norwegian American Newspaper, *Skandinaven* at $6 per week – meager earnings, perhaps. But he still managed to put aside $1 of his pay every week, allowing himself only such comparatively small luxuries as 10 cents for fresh fruit and some smoking tobacco every week.

In the Spring of 1890, after he had advanced to $12 a week, considered a fair wage at that time, he married a cute schoolmate from Norway – Therese Korsvik – and their marriage was eventually blessed with three children.

Later Osland became associated with Charles Wacker, a brewer, renowned for his part in the Burnham-Wacker Chicago beautification plan and for whom Wacker Drive was named. Osland's career took off and was never headed.

His energy and leadership were unlimited. Scarcely a club or society connected with the Norwegian colony existed in which Birger Osland did not have a "finger in the pie." These included the Dovre Political Club, Chicago Norske Club, Kvartett Klubben, Norwegian American Historical Society, and the Pioneer Club and he was in on the ground floor in the organization of the Norwegian American Steamship Line.

He then founded his own company – Birger Osland and Co., Inc., Investment Bankers with offices on LaSalle Street. Then in 1917 he was named assistant military attache with the American legation in Oslo and in 1929 he was elected a trustee for the Century of Progress World's Fair held in Chicago in 1933 and 1934.

In his autobiography, Osland expressed the philosophy which was a key to his active and humanitarian life: "I had no conviction whatever that my own difficulties were caused by 'social maladjustments' or 'world conditions', nor did I feel that the world owed me a living unless I earned it. I was too busy looking for a better job...There are those who feel discontent because they do not enjoy the privileges of a high position and a large income, a fine home, opportunity to travel and to wear fine clothes...although they seem to lack the ability and perseverance required to earn it by their own self-discipline...as many have done and anyone may do in this free land. Sound common sense is a rather rare commodity in this world, and has been so ever since Mother Eve handed Adam the apple in the Garden of Eden."

Osland's death in 1963 at the age of 93 brought a flood of condolences and messages of praise from all over the world.

It was put most succinctly and appropriately by Dr. Lichtenstein, who wrote at the time: "Birger Osland aligned himself with the field of human endeavor that contributed little to the sufferings of man, but added much to a longer and healthier life with relief from pain and suffering. He witnessed the benefits of anesthesia, antisepsis, and the technology of surgery, all of which developed in his lifetime.

"The identification of bacteria, the diseases they produced, and the development of serums, biologicals and chemicals for their elimination, also took place in this lifetime. He witnessed the discovery and the use of hormones, enzymes, and vitamins, and he saw the gradual departure of cholera, plague, typhoid and many other infectious diseases.

"The notable achievements in public health and preventive medicine, the establishment of nurses training schools, the Red Cross, modern medical schools and the methods of instant communication of the advances and discoveries were also a contribution in this fruitful period of world history."

"Happy indeed were the eyes fortunate enough to see all of this," Lichtenstein concluded.

Isak B. Faleide

Mr. Faleide, who in the course of his residence in Chicago was involved in several Norwegian social clubs as well as professional organizations, was born in 1881 at Faleide, Nordfjord, his family's ancestral home for centuries.

Like so many gifted and able young men from the fjords, he went to the city of Bergen to obtain his education in his chosen field of engineering, graduating in 1902 from the famous Bergen Tekniske Skole. He then emigrated immediately to the United States, arriving in Chicago in 1902 and obtaining his first job in the States in the Waukegan shop of American Steel & Wire Co. He soon moved back to Chicago where he was employed for several years by Western Electric Company.

His professional career really began in 1904 when he joined the staff of such nationally known engineering and construction firms as John S. Metcalfe Co., Construction Engineers (1904-1906) and James Stewart Co. (1906-1911). In 1911, he became the chief engineer of the Burrell Engineering & Construction Co. before joining the staff of Folwell Engineering Co. as chief engineer in 1916, where he remained until 1938 as Vice President and partner of the firm.

Then in 1938, he realized the dream of a lifetime to head his own firm and he formed the Faleide Engineering Co. of Chicago. The firm was involved in construction projects from coast to coast building industrial plants, flour mills, cement plants, grain elevators, feed mills and coal handling operations, among others.

The year 1904 was marked by his marriage to Bertha, or Bee as she was known to friends and associates, the dream girl of his youth, who is fondly remembered for her personality and as a tireless worker, all of which established her as a leader in the Norwegian community in Chicago.

Faleide and his wife Bee took active roles in Norwegian affairs, clubs and institutions in Chicago. They were parents of three children, a daughter Bergliot (Bibbs), and two sons, Roy and Norman, as well as several grandchildren.

Isak Faleide was a charter member of the Norwegian American Engineering Society, which he served as President for three years. In 1911 he became active in the Chicago Norske Klub and served the CNK as its president during the difficult years of 1929-30.

But perhaps his greatest contribution in terms of active volunteer service was the countless hours that he contributed to Norwegian American Hospital both as board trustee and as President from 1948 to 1954, a period of significant expansion in the history of the hospital.

A visitor to his homeland on more than one occasion, he received the Knight's Cross of the Order of St. Olaw in 1954, for his dedication to various Norwegian causes during a full and active lifetime. Isak Faleide passed away in 1964.

Dr. Manuel E. Lichtenstein

"A great surgeon, teacher, humanitarian..." so reads a scroll presented to Dr. Manuel E. Lichtenstein, on January 14, 1959 by his fellow staffers at Norwegian American Hospital. The words speak eloquently of the high esteem felt by Dr. Lichtenstein's associates back in the '50s and '60s.

Born in Chicago on August 15, 1900, of immigrant parents, Dr. Lichtenstein's youth was fairly normal. To supplement the meager family income, young Lichtenstein delivered newspapers and shined shoes. His father was a tobacco merchant on Chicago Avenue, and the family income was modest to say the least.

After attending Tuley High School, Lichtenstein went on to the University of Chicago then to medical school at the famous Rush Medical College. With his father in poor health, and visits by doctors to the family home fairly frequent, times were hard. But so impressed was the young Lichtenstein with the skills and compassion of the doctors that attended his father that he there and then decided that medicine would be his profession.

After graduating with his M.D. degree from Rush in 1925 (he also held an M.S. degree in physiology from Northwestern University), he fulfilled his internship and residency requirements at the Cook County Hospital, then one of the finest institutions in the country for postgraduate training.

He then launched a medical career which at various times saw him as a teacher at Northwestern University's School of Medicine, army surgeon (on the

Italian front during World War II) and a senior attending physician at among others, Norwegian American Hospital, Cook County, and Michael Reese.

During a six year period (from 1959 to 1964) he was chairman of the Department of Surgery at Cook County, and Norwegian American had him aboard as a member of the medical staff from January 1, 1935 until he died on December 3, 1977.

World War II proved a highlight in a career already distinguished through his lectures, writing and knowledge of medicine. As a member of the U.S. armed forces, he landed with the assault troops at Anzio, and was often subjected to mortar and artillery fire. For performing with uncommon dedication and valor he was awarded the Bronze Star by General Mark Clark "for meritorious services in support of combat operations in Italy from September 9, 1943 to June 5, 1944."

But that was not his only award, not by far. Brazil, which also had troops involved in the Italian campaign, awarded Lichtenstein one of its highest honors, the Medal de Guerra for "organizing the medical staff of the Brazilian Expeditionary Force and successfully establishing the practice of modern surgical methods for the care of battle casualties among the Brazilian troops."

Subsequently, he was further honored by the Brazilian doctors who had served under him during the crucial months in the Italian campaign. Among others he was invited to serve as a visiting professor of surgery at the University of Brazil and presented an honorary degree of Doctor of Honoris Causa.

"To remember is to live," were the words honoring him at a banquet in his honor, "and we shall never forget the hundreds of Brazilian wounded who had their lives saved thanks to your intelligence, your devotion and your valor in providing equal treatment to all who were brought to you..."

Since those times, Dr. Lichtenstein made great contributions in the world of medicine, not only as an accomplished and highly skilled surgeon, but as a teacher, author and lecturer. Over the years, he diagrammed carefully every operation he ever performed, for research purposes in case he should ever want to review his past operations.

As a teacher, he helped teach a generation of physicians. And as a lecturer he was in constant demand, appearing numerous times before medical and surgical groups all over the world.

Nor were his talents confined to the operating room or the lecture hall. He was equally good as a writer. A productive, clear and committed writer, he was author of more than 100 medical papers, dealing primarily with various aspects of surgery and with the ethical and philosophical aspects of medicine.

Busy as he was, Lichtenstein found time to belong to many professional bodies in his field, including such well known agencies as the AMA, American College of Surgeons (he was a past vice president of the Metropolitan Chicago chapter) and a past vice president of the Illinois Surgical Society, and a former vice president of the International College of Surgeons, and active in many other professional groups.

His work left him with very little time for recreation, but following his retirement, he found time for travel, a very esteemed pursuit for both he and his wife. His favorite destination: Yellowstone National Park or the Black Hills of North Dakota. Travel and his relationships with his seven grandchildren were his favorite pleasures.

As the renowned poet and writer, Robert Louis Stevenson, put it so well, "There are men who stand above the common herd." Such a man was Dr. Lichtenstein who stood tall with those whose lives he made better through his genius and compassion. He truly was one of Norwegian American Hospital's great men of medicine. Dr. Lichtenstein died after a lingering illness in 1977 at the age of 77.

Dr. Anton M. Jensen

During a highly active career which spanned more than 45 years, Dr. Anton Jensen, joined the medical staff at Norwegian American Hospital in 1936. This was a period when scarcely anyone could afford hospital care. And many hospitals were virtually empty and many physicians unpaid.

Despite the economic crunch, the Danish born physician, enjoyed a busy medical

practice as in his own words: "I took care of the Danish community. Sometimes I was paid, but often I didn't charge for my services."

It was practices such as Jensen's which helped keep hospitals like Norwegian American alive during the Depression. His loyal service to the Danish community did not go unrewarded. In 1959 he had the honor of receiving one of Denmark's oldest and highest awards for his service in promoting Danish American interests. The award, conferred by Denmark's Frederik IX, is given for excellence in civilian or military service.

In addition, in 1976, Dr. Jensen was honored with the Dane of the Year award from the Danish National Committee.

Born in Denmark on a farm near Granslev in 1892, Jensen was the youngest of 10 children. It was during this period that his interest in things medical first became apparent as he helped to deliver small calves, lambs and colts. "I enjoyed those experiences and decided that I wanted to be a veterinarian. I later changed my mind and decided to become a doctor instead."

After completing a three-year course in medicine in a college near his home town, Jensen took the grueling medical examination for admission to the medical college of the University of Copenhagen and was accepted. There then began a 12-year period of study ending in 1927, a program which included four years of graduate study in surgery and one year in internal medicine.

Following completion of his medical training, Jensen applied for a teaching position in the medical college of the University of Copenhagen which failed to materialize so he decided instead to come to America. After visiting hospitals in New York and Michigan, he was drawn to Chicago where he had many friends in the Danish community.

Although Chicago would eventually become his home, Jensen left the city after a brief stay to join the practice of a friend, Dr. Charles Bray, in a small community located near Duluth, Minnesota. And it was there that Jensen vividly recalled the harsh winters of Northern Minnesota. "I remember driving 40 miles in below zero temperatures to deliver a baby." By the time he reached his destination his hands were so frozen, he could barely move them.

The area was also dangerous, as Jensen recalled, noting that "one winter day, I got out of the car to take a walk in the area," only to be approached by a farmer armed with a gun who warned him to get back in the car "because I was being eyed by a pack of wolves."

A scant six months after this episode, Jensen found himself in the Hawaiian Islands. "I worked in Lihue Hospital on Kauai, one of the northwestern islands," he said.

He had planned to make Hawaii his home, but wound up instead back in Chicago out of loyalty to the Danish community. "A friend in Chicago asked me to help him with his medical practice, so I returned," he said.

After settling in Chicago once again, he met his wife and they were married in 1942 making their home at Kedzie and North Avenues, not far from the hospital. They later moved to River Forest, and were parents of a daughter, Toni, a special education teacher in Chicago.

In spite of his long years of medical practice in the States, Dr. Jensen never forgot his Danish roots. In 1961 he donated an elaborate carillon to the family church near Graslev, Denmark in memory of his parents. The 14 bell set weighing 800 pounds can play some 200 musical selections on the carillon which is connected to the church organ.

In 1977, Dr. Jensen, at 85 years of age, noted that medicine had changed significantly during his more than 50 years of practice. "Perhaps the most noticeable change is increasing specialization," he said, adding that he had been trained to do general abdominal surgery. "Now there are specialists in heart surgery, organ transplants and other surgical techniques," he noted.

The hospital too has changed, he said, adding that additions had enlarged the original hospital structures, resulting in larger number of patient beds and a much larger staff. Likewise, medical care has witnessed many new treatment techniques and the introduction of sophisticated electronic equipment.

Even so the hospital's continued success over the years is due in large part to physicians such as Dr. Jensen, who helped the hospital in its early years and continued their dedicated service in the decades to follow. He died in 1987 at the ripe old age of 95.

Dr. James P. Ahstrom

A story in the Fall 1977 issue of the *Lamp* describes Dr. James P. Ahstrom, then 90 and in his second year of retirement (after more than a half century of treating patients at Norwegian American) as still mentally alert, although slowed somewhat by a recent stroke. "But he still is keenly interested in the medical profession he has served with such ...distinction," the story continues.

Among the amusing anecdotes which Ahstrom vividly recalled is running against the famous Notre Dame football coach, Knute Rockne, "the slowest half miler I ever saw."

Though fairly diminutive in size, the story continues, Dr. Ahstrom in his youth was quite an athlete who was active in bowling, baseball, football and handball.

The story tells of his recollection of a sandlot football game for the city championship won by a 3-0 dropkick. In bowling, although he never rolled a 300 game, he came close. And in baseball, he must have been quite a slugger. He chuckled, the story notes, over exaggerations by one admirer that "he hit the ball so far it took a half hour to bring it back."

But it was medicine, not athletics, to which Dr. Ahstrom gave his long and productive life. He recalled, the story says, floating around in a washtub to escape the floods which deluged Northern Germany, where he was born in 1887. His father, a former German soldier, was a tanner, but business was stagnant, so in 1890, he uprooted his family and though his wife was pregnant, came to America, arriving in Duluth, Minnesota together with a new daughter born on the high seas.

But business was hardly any better in Duluth, so the family moved first to Milwaukee, where young Ahstrom started school, and then to Chicago.

It was the family physician who first induced young Ahstrom to consider medicine as a career. He was working as a bank messenger around the turn of the century and after, as he put it: "after drinking beer and eating the free food in the neighborhood saloon," he would stop by the office of the doctor, near Chicago and Milwaukee Avenues.

Then in 1908, with the doctor's help, he enrolled in the medical school at Fulton and Ada Streets (later Loyola Medical School) and he recalls his bank supervisor's reaction when Ahstrom advised him that he planned to leave to attend medical school. "What do you want to do that for," the cashier said somewhat out of sorts. "You're just becoming valuable to us."

Among his many recollections, Dr. Ahstrom remembered long evenings spent on the Wabash Avenue El platform watching the rats, and showing passengers silent movies, a chore for which he received the grand sum of $1 a night.

Later came a stint in local politics in behalf of William Hale "Big Bill" Thompson, the late Mayor of Chicago. He recalls standing on a soapbox enumerating the merits of Big Bill to a noon-hour crowd. "I couldn't tell if I was being booed or applauded," he smiled.

After completing medical school in 1912, Ahstrom interned at St. Bernard's Hospital on the south side for a year, receiving no salary for the honor, only room and board. In January 1914 he opened his office at North Avenue near Crawford – the first of several offices he was to maintain on North Avenue during the next 62 years.

He became a member of the medical staff at Norwegian American in 1925 and vividly recalls his first patient at the hospital – an appendicitis case. But it was the day after that really stuck in his mind at NAH. As he put it: "I delivered one baby, got some sleep, then deliver another baby, got some sleep and would go at it again. I decided then that I didn't want to do that forever. It could kill you."

But hard work proved no obstacle to this dedicated doctor, as the years went by. He made house calls until about 1967 and subsequently held nearly every office of the NAH medical staff including President in 1955. He also taught pediatrics at a clinic for physicians in Chicago, and was active in various medical societies, subsequently serving as chief of the medical staff of Chicago's Medinah Temple of the Shrine.

Somehow he managed to find time to marry (his wife, Anna, died in 1974) and to father one son, James Ahstrom Jr, who "wanted to be a doctor just like his father," and who subsequently went on to become an orthopedic surgeon and a former member of the NAH medical staff, and a daughter, Grace, who married an insurance executive and worked for a small town newspaper for many years. After a long and very productive medical career of 62 years, the good doctor died at age 92 in 1979.

Dr. George T. Murphy

Hardworking, productive and versatile are just a few of the words that come to mind to describe Dr. George T. Murphy. After joining the medical staff at NAH, in 1933, at the height of the Depression, Dr. Murphy maintained his affiliation with the hospital for more than 40 years.

In this period at Norwegian American, he served a one-year term as medical staff president, chaired the Surgery Department, created the Tissue Committee, developed a surgical residency program and gave generously of his time and talents to various other hospital and medical staff functions.

He was appointed Director of Medical Education in December 1970, a post he held for several years, in the course of which he created a surgical residency program. In 1977, following 37 years of sterling service to the hospital and more than 52 years in medical practice, Dr. Murphy retired to enjoy some well-deserved years of recreation and rest in Florida, with his wife, Leone.

Born in 1898 in Chicago, the son of a batallion chief in the Chicago Fire Department, one might assume that the young man would follow in his father's footsteps or in city service. But this was not to be.

When the lad was about 8 or 9 he had a chance to hitch up a horse named Topsy, he recalls, and "chauffeur" a local doctor, Dr. Latimer, in his buggy to the hospital every day for the great sum of 5 cents a trip. As a result he grew fond of the good doctor and decided to emulate him by choosing medicine as a career.

"I can recall when I was in high school (Schurz) that I used to sneak by the guards at County Hospital to watch the operations," Dr. Murphy said.

After graduating from Schurz in 1916, he entered the University of Illinois, then served for a year as a field artillery officer at Ft. Sheridan and Camp Taylor.

Completing his college work at the University of Illinois in 1920, he went on for his medical degree at Rush Medical College, then affiliated with the University of Chicago. He completed his internship both at Highland Park and Cook County Hospitals in 1927.

This was followed by four years at the famed Mayo Clinic in Rochester, Minnesota, where he received his master of science degree in surgery in 1931. It was while in Rochester that he met a young school teacher, Leone Baihly, who two years later was to become his bride.

In 1931 during the darkest period of the Depression, he took charge of a heavily mortgaged 40-bed hospital in Oakes, North Dakota. Money was very tight at the time, and payments for services equally tight. So in 1932 he returned to Chicago, where the prospects for a young doctor just starting out in practice were not much brighter.

"I made relief calls for $1.50 in those days," he recalls, adding that "the fee included the cost of medicines."

Later, as his career grew, Dr. Murphy developed a fondness for the outdoors, especially for hunting in Canada, Minnesota and Wisconsin.

His professional affiliations over the years included memberships on the medical staffs of St. Anne's and Swedish Covenant Hospitals as well as the American College of Surgeons, the AMA, Sigma Xi, the Illinois State and the Chicago Medical Societies and the Alumni Association of the Mayo Foundation.

Shortly before he died in 1990 at the grand age of 91, he told an interviewer that certain aspects of medicine had changed little over the decades and "look and feel the same."

"It must not be forgotten," he said, "that many basic clinical skills are virtually changeless. A good history, a good physical exam, and a sensible plan of study are the basis of an effective medical practice."

Dr. Helen Louise Button

From her earliest years on a Pennsylvania farm, Helen Louise Button had no intention of restricting her life to home and hearthside.

Her father, a staunch believer in "women's lib" maintained that women could do anything, "even becoming president of the United States." It was an opinion fully shared with Dr. Button's mother, a teacher in a little one-room schoolhouse in Northeastern Pennsylvania.

If that was not enough, the little town where she grew up was home to one of the few female doctors practicing in Pennsylvania at that time. It would seem that young Helen was destined to become a physician.

Helen Louise Button, "Dockie" to her friends, was about the 10th or 11th generation of her family born on American soil and she had an ancestor who had gravitated to this country eight years after the *Mayflower* had supposedly landed at Plymouth Rock.

The young Helen, lively as her perky surname, went to local schools, hunted ducks with her doctor friend, galloped across the Pennsylvania hills on horseback, and anchored several positions on the girl's baseball team.

After finishing high school, her mother convinced her to attend a teacher's college in Westchester, PA, even though her heart was set on a medical career. Helen's mother figured that she could always teach and that a medical degree would be too great a strain on the family resources. But eventually Helen's wishes prevailed and she spent her junior and senior years at the University of Pennsylvania where she graduated in 1922 with a bachelor's degree in science.

Following a four-year interval, she came to Chicago where she taught and took courses in chemistry, physics and science at the University of Chicago in preparation for a medical degree. In 1926 she was accepted for a five year internship at Lutheran Memorial Hospital where she graduated in 1930.

From then, her achievements and appointments followed in quick and assured order starting with the completion of her residency requirements in obstetrics and gynecology at Cook County Hospital. She then did some postgraduate work under Drs. Richard Jafee and Walter Schiller followed by postgraduate work under the well known Dr. Bertha Van Hoosen of Mary Thompson Hospital. There Dr. Van Hoosen referred to Helen as one of her "surgical daughters" in her book, *Pettycoat Surgeon.*

In 1941 she joined the staff at Norwegian American Hospital where she remained until 1945, leaving to help start a women's medical center at Mary Thompson Hospital. She rejoined the NAH staff in 1967 because of its "excellent medical education program." During the War years, with many male doctors in the service, she was placed in charge of the Outpatient Gynecology Clinic at Cook County Hospital – treating as many as 120 patients on some days, she recalled.

During the '40s she taught at Cook County Graduate School and since 1954 she was on the surgical faculty at Chicago Medical School. From 1952 to 1954, she was a surgical resident at American Hospital and she did postgraduate study at the University of Vienna. (She was later chosen vice-president of the American Medical Society of Vienna.)

Among her more colorful assignments were three months spent in 1946 touring the hospitals of South America and in 1963 she accepted a three-month's assignment at a 160-bed hospital in Nigeria for a Lutheran mission.

"It was an unforgettable human adventure," she is quoted as saying. "We started operating at 5:30, four days a week. Breakfast at nine, operate again until one, lunch, then back to work at the clinic until five. After that, rounds with the patients."

The story continued with her recollections of medical problems encountered. "Almost everyone from infancy on eats nothing but 'gari' or tapioca and this can cause terrible cases of hernia. We would get worm infestation from people drinking unboiled river water and we saw people in dreadful agony – perhaps a spitting cobra had spit venom in an eye. We would get endless streams of children in advanced stages of 'kwashiorkor,' a protein deficiency ailment that caused swelling all over the body, running sores, and stupor."

Despite all of this activity, she still found time to marry Isadore Goldstein, a criminal lawyer, in 1939, and had two children, Morris and Alvin. The former was an orthopedic surgeon at the Shriners Hospital in Chicago, and the younger boy was attending law school in Atlanta.

For recreation, she liked to ride horseback and took flying lessons to qualify her for a pilot's license until some "acrobatics in a tailspin with her husband as a passenger put that hobby in a tailspin." In 1962, while studying medicine in Vienna, she bought a Lippizaner mare and embarked on a side career breeding horses.

Her professional activities included serving as vice president of the prestigious American Women's Medical Association and she was a founding member of the Business and Professional Women's Club.

After her husband died in 1964 she maintained offices in the Loop and lived, as she had for many years, in a rambling, stucco home in the Austin area of Chicago where she had the company of four dogs, including a Basenji pup she brought home from Nigeria and a parrot from Brazil. Rounding out the Button menagerie were six horses that she kept stabled near Libertyville.

As to the future, she planned to continue her full-time medical practice with emphasis on teaching and surgery and intended to devote more time to foreign missions. But her death in 1995 put an end to her ideas of serving in a Lutheran mission in Madras, India.

Dr. Rasmus J. Harr

"Last summer," begins the story in the Spring 1973 *Lamp*, "In New York City's prestigious Madison Square Garden, the American Academy of Family Practice conferred the degree of Fellow upon 4,200 of its more active and illustrious members for outstanding efforts in the area of continuing education."

"Among the recipients," the story notes, "appropriately attired in academic robe, mortarboard, and wearing the Academy's gold and blue colors, was our own Rasmus Joachim Harr, a member of the NAH medical staff since 1967, one of the city's distinguished general practitioners, and a prominent personality in Midwest America's Norwegian community."

The story went on to note that this was just one of many honors and awards received in a notable medical career dating back to 1936, the year he received his M.D. degree from the Loyola University School of Medicine. He was knighted for example, by the King of Norway (The Royal Order of Olaw), honored with awards and medals from the Federation of Norsemen, the Sons of Norway, and other Norwegian organizations. During World War II, he had been decorated with the South Pacific War Medal and the Philippines Liberation

Medal. He had in addition served as president of the Pioneer Club, an organization that went back 92 years, and of the 500 member Federation of Norsemen.

That Norway was a dominant part of Dr. Harr's life seems obvious. He was born in 1908 in the land of the fjords, mountains and the midnight sun into an old and prominent family that could trace its roots back to the year 1545. For the first 15 years of his life, through high school and a few farm jobs, Norway was home. Then, when America beckoned in 1928, young Harr listed on his visa as a farmhand, entered the United States through the port of New York and traveled on to Chicago. Factory jobs, not farm labor, were far more plentiful in the Chicago of those days, so young Harr began his American experience spray-painting telephones at Western Electric. His dream however remained a career in medicine, and through the Depression years, he struggled evenings attending first Crane Junior College and then Loyola's School of Medicine in fulfilling medicine's requirements which even then were lengthy, costly and strenuous.

Following an internship at Lutheran Deaconess Hospital, Dr. Harr hung up his shingle as a general practitioner. World War II intervened unfortunately, putting a temporary halt to his private practice and a few years later, Dr. Harr was in uniform serving as a captain with the U.S. Army Medical Corps and a member of such renowned fighting outfits as the ski troopers of the 2nd Division and the 11th Army Corps.

In 1943-44 he was stationed in New Guinea, then the Philippines and other exotic islands of the South Pacific. He vividly recalled an episode where Japanese troops penetrated the American lines and forced an immediate evacuation of 100 American soldiers.

But it was not long after that he was able to exchange his army uniforms for civilian attire and to pick up his medical career where he had left off. And an exceptional career it was, including as it did many years as voluntary house doctor of a children's home for as many as 140 boys and girls, and more than 35 years as the voluntary medical director of the Bethesda Old People's Home, a position he still held at the time of the *Lamp* story.

"I have never forgotten my Dad's example when it came to helping the poor and the sick," he explained, adding, "that it was in his blood."

Professionally, he was a member of the medical staffs of both NAH and Lutheran General Hospital. At NAH he was serving his second term as staff treasurer and chairman of the Finance Committee as well as being active on several other committees. His professional memberships included the AMA, the Chicago and Illinois State Medical Societies, and the American Academy of Family Practice.

Despite his lengthy list of professional and volunteer activities, the good doctor still found time to start a family with his wife Gudrun (the daughter of a well known Norwegian pastor) and the marriage was blessed with six children: a son, Roald, and five lovely daughters: Karen, Joann, Solveig, Ingrid and Kristin.

Even though the children were married or away at school, the Harrs still maintained a richly appointed, ranch home in Park Ridge, just north of Lutheran General Hospital and a lakeside year round summer home near Antioch, Illinois, where they could indulge their enjoyment of motor boating and a more leisurely lifestyle. Death cut short his retirement years. He passed away in October of 1976.

Dr. Isadore Isoe

For our profile of Dr. Isoe, one of the great surgeons practicing at NAH during the period, we again go to the summer 1977 issue of the *Lamp* which begins: "Tributes are rare in any profession, but this past April 17 more than 700 patients, and friends gathered at Antoine's cavernous banquet hall in Chicago to pay a surprise tribute...to one of Norwegian American Hospital's great men of medicine – Dr. Isadore M. Isoe.

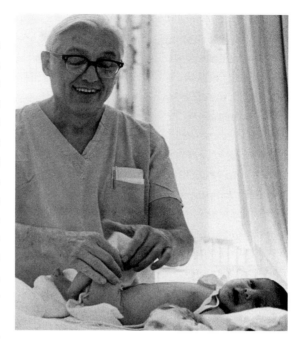

"It was a surprising and unusual affair, certainly one of the largest gatherings of its type ever held for any doctor in Chicago. In addition to a plaque, Dr. Isoe received a memory book containing the names and tributes of well-wishers and donations in his honor of more than $3,300 for use of the hospital for surgical improvements and a standing sentimental tribute from every person in the hall."

"It was a well-deserved honor for the quiet and unassuming surgeon who considers every patient his friend."

Born in Chicago in 1913 of immigrant parents from Romania, Dr. Isoe grew up in Humboldt Park and worked in the area virtually his entire life. He attended Lowell grammar school and Tuley High School , where he was an unusually good student. He represented his school in nationwide competitive exams. Although he didn't win, he considered it quite an honor.

He then applied to four medical schools, being accepted by all, but ending up at the School of Medicine at the University of Illinois because its tuition was considerably lower than the others. After receiving his M.D. degree at Illinois in 1937, he interned at Cook County, then completed a residency in surgery at University Hospital, a small hospital then located near Cook County Hospital.

With World War II imminent, he enlisted in the service in 1941 and for the next four and a half years the military was his assignment. He spent three of those years in New Guinea, Australia and the Philippines. He vividly recalls, the *Lamp* notes, performing surgery underground with Japanese bombs bursting overhead, and once operating for 72 hours straight without a break. Possibly his strangest mission, he recalls, was a two-week advance medical assignment with Philippine guerillas on an island scheduled for invasion by U.S. troops.

The equipment was primitive. Surgery was performed in a portable surgical hospital with tents providing shelter, portable lanterns and flashlights the lighting. He recalls chasing flies away from the wounds of the men being treated and other procedures not recommended by the AMA.

By discharge date, in 1946, he was a major and he returned for another year of postgraduate study at the University of Illinois and the second year of his surgical residency at NAH. He then began his practice as a general practitioner and a surgeon with offices on North Elston Avenue.

But the year previous, he had met and married a young nurse on the staff at Illinois Masonic Hospital. Dr. Isoe and his wife, Laura, were parents of three adult children: Linda, a surgical nurse in San Francisco; Mitchell, who was working on an advanced degree in environmental science and Cynthia, (whom Dr. Isoe delivered himself when the obstetrician was late in arriving), who was a student of occupational therapy and a part-time business office employee at the hospital.

After passing his boards in 1949, Dr. Isoe spent several years in various positions, first as chairman of surgery at Doctor's Hospital and then on the surgical staff of Chicago Medical School. He had been on the NAH medical staff for nearly 30 years, serving as chairman of numerous committees and a term as president.

For 10 years, he had served as chairman of the surgery department. He was also a charter member of the American Society of Abdominal Surgeons and a member of the American Medical Association. Following his retirement several years ago, Dr. Isoe continued to make his home in Lincolnwood where for years he followed his hobbies of reading (science fiction and mysteries) duplicate bridge and collecting oriental art, up until the time of his death in February of 1999 at 85 years old.

"It was quite a thrill seeing all of those people, for a man who believes with all of his heart in the 10 commandments, a man who considers most of his patients as his friends, a man who is truly one of our hospital's great men of medicine, ...such honor wasn't much of a surprise."

On April 29, 1977, the Illinois State Senate joined in presenting the doctor with a resolution which reads: "as a lasting expression of the respect and esteem held for this outstanding physician, surgeon, and human being by the members of this chamber."

Dr. Aaron Learner

"A dedicated man of medicine and a distinguished scientist, who will not accept or countenance incompetence in a field of medicine where mistakes cannot be permitted..." so one might describe Dr. Aaron Learner, for many years the Director of the Pathology Department and the clinical laboratories at Norwegian American Hospital.

Dr. Learner's thirst for knowledge and his ability worked to his advantage in advancing through Chicago's public schools and Crane Junior College to the University of Illinois on a scholarship.

At the University's School of Medicine, his impressive record gained him nomination to two prestigious medical honorary societies: Alpha Omega Alpha and Sigma Xi.

In particular, he recalled two professors at the University who had a profound impact on him – Dr. Richard H. Jaffe, head of the school's department of Pathology, who helped shape his future career, and Dr. Sterling Lamprecht, head of the Department of Philosophy (later chairman of the Department of Philosophy at Amherst College in New York), who inspired in Dr. Learner a lifelong interest in mental discipline involved in acquiring wisdom and knowledge.

But as was the case of so many young men of the era, World War II intervened in 1942 and he enlisted as an officer in the U.S. Medical Corps. His responsibilities in the service involved setting up and running a hospital at Camp Campbell, Kentucky. Later he was placed in charge of pathology departments for Army hospitals in France and Italy.

At the war's end he served for a while as chief pathologist at Oak Ridge (Tennessee) Hospital. In 1947 he returned to Chicago and accepted a post at NAH which he held through 1970. He recalls that to gain the post he was interviewed and recommended for the position by the famous Dr. Ludvig Hektoen. No one, he chuckled, would ever question a recommendation of Dr. Hektoen's and accordingly he was hired without a hitch.

Somewhere in his busy schedule, Dr. Learner found time to marry and to raise a family of three children – two daughters, one married to a high school teacher; the other a recent graduate of Boston University with ambitions to pursue a career in the fine arts; and a son who is a museum curator.

In his dual role as head of NAH's department of Pathology, and a member of the University of Illinois where he was associate professor of pathology, Dr. Learner had very little time to pursue his favorite hobbies, photography and reading; but the lab remained his life.

And it was in the lab, that Dr. Learner foresaw tremendous changes coming as more and more highly automated equipment and procedures are unveiled to make the laboratory more efficient and effective.

While this is bound to create some "soul searching as things change," he said, "he feels that the lab will always relate to the doctor."

As he put it, "The relationship between the lab and the doctor should always be complementary – never competitive."

Dr. Bernard Kleppel

Man of science, brilliant diagnostician and humanitarian – these were just a few of the qualities which combined in Bernard Kleppel, long-time director of Radiology during the 1960s to make him a distinguished member of the NAH medical staff.

To illustrate, we quote the Winter 1972 *Lamp* which describes a passage which Dr. Kleppel penned to his wife Lucy and his daughters, Judy, Lucy and Reva early in 1970. "They were words that flowed from the heart and which reached his family only by accident when the notebook in which the passage was written was found on his desk following his death."

"I am deeply thankful and appreciative of the blessings that you, my precious treasured family, have afforded me." So begins the passage which is quoted in the *Lamp*. "No one could ask for more. I have tried to be as good and loving a husband and father as possible. I have tried to prepare you for a good life ahead and would hope that you would honor me by continuing to be kind and loving and protective of one another, by trusting and being responsible for one another during times of joy and distress."

"I pray that you may never know want or hunger, or loss of your freedom to live in security, and that you may never know the horror of war or the ravages of disease. May you be blessed with peace, plenty, health, and long years filled with the satisfaction of many accomplishments...

"Leave the world a little better, a little cleaner, a little freer and more prosperous than you found it...."

Far too soon after these words were written...death came to Dr. Bernard Kleppel, closing the career of a man who was not only one of our hospital's great men of medicine, but who did indeed leave the world a little better, a little cleaner, a little friendlier, and a little more compassionate.

Born in New York City in 1918, the fourth of five children, Kleppel earned his bachelor's degree in social science from City College of New York, then studied electrical engineering at Pratt Institute.

Following several years as an engineer with a transformer company in New York during World War II, Kleppel made the switch to medicine, finishing his pre-med at New York University and completing in 1945 his academic requirements at Chicago Medical School, where he was second scholastically in his class and president of the graduating class.

His primary interest was pediatrics at the time, but after an internship and residency at Mt. Sinai Hospital, he concluded that a less strenuous field of medicine was desirable. Then, partly because of his background in electronics, he decided to join the staff at the University of Minnesota's Hospital complex where he studied under the famous Dr. Leo Rigler.

In 1956 he returned to Chicago, and until 1962 was connected with Michael Reese Hospital as assistant medical director of the Radiology Department.

"His talents as a teacher, a gentleman and a superb radiologist became known to the entire staff during this period," said his good friend and associate, Dr. Harvey White, of Children's Memorial Hospital.

On April 1, 1962, Dr. Kleppel joined the medical staff of NAH and was appointed director of radiology, a position he held for nine years until his death.

At Norwegian American, to quote Dr. White again, "Bernie excelled as a fine human being, a radiologist, and a teacher of interns, residents and hospital staff. Because of his vast knowledge of medicine, he was frequently consulted by staff on many difficult problems. His forte in radiology was the gastrointestinal tract, and his ability in this field was recognized by his peers."

Dr. Kleppel's professional background included being named a Diplomate of the Board of Radiology in 1955. He was also a member of the Radiological Society of North America, the American Medical Association and the local radiological society. He was at the time of his death an assistant professor of radiology at the Chicago Medical School.

Dr. August Daro

Author, expert on delivery of babies, women's diseases and even golf – those were a few of the distinctions of Dr. August Daro. Dr. Daro, who was on the medical staff at Norwegian American during the '60s and '70s, was chairman emeritus of obstetrics and gynecology at Columbus/Cuneo/Cabrini Medical Center and a former professor of obstetrics and gynecology at Cook County Graduate School of Medicine and the Stritch School of Medicine of Loyola University.

Daro, who lived in Wilmette, was author of two books, one published at the time of his death in 1986, *Dr. Daro's Nutrition Prescriptions for Your Common Health Problems*, and a golf book, *The Inside Swing*.

Born in Crotone, Italy in 1900, Dr. Daro graduated from the Chicago Medical School in 1925. He then interned at Illinois Masonic Hospital and did his residency at Chicago Lying-In Hospital, followed by postgraduate work in England and Vienna.

For more than 20 years he was on the staff at Cook County Hospital and once in 1930 showed his courage by helping to subdue an armed robber in a tussle outside of the hospital. A long-time associate of Dr. Karl Meyer, the hospital's renowned superintendent for many years, Dr. Daro helped organize the hospital's gynecological clinic. He married Meyer's daughter, Maryann in 1947, and she preceded him in death in 1976.

In a lifetime full of achievement, Dr. Daro found time to publish numerous scientific papers on obstetrics and gynecology and won many awards. In 1967, he was appointed to the advisory board of the state Public Health Department.

The year preceding his death in 1986, a newspaper reporter found Daro volunteering to teach golf to psychiatric patients on an indoor putting range at the Lakeside Veterans Administration Hospital.

"I think there is a kind of family feeling for veterans," he said, adding that, "I wanted to do something for veterans." He had served in the U.S. Army Air Corps during World War II from 1942 to 1945, primarily at a base in Wisconsin, where he had the distinction of delivering more than 2,000 babies to military families.

He was survived by a son, Karl M., and a daughter, Pamela Ann Case and four grandchildren.